HIERARCHICAL STRUCTURE:

A Model of Design and Planning Processes

Date Due

M.I.T. REPORT NO. 7.

HIERARCHICAL STRUCTURE:

A Model of Design and Planning Processes

Marvin L. Manheim

THE M.I.T. PRESS
Massachusetts Institute of Technology
Cambridge, Massachusetts, and London, England

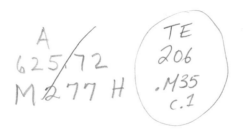
Research Report No. R64-15
Massachusetts Institute of Technology
Cambridge, Massachusetts
May 1964

Library of Congress Catalog Card Number: 66-28895
Printed in the United States of America

Submitted to the Department of Civil Engineering on May 15, 1964
in partial fulfillment of the requirements for the degree of
Doctor of Philosophy under the title:

HIGHWAY ROUTE LOCATION AS A HIERARCHICALLY STRUCTURED
SEQUENTIAL DECISION PROCESS:

An experiment in the use of Bayesian decision theory
for guiding an engineering process

by

MARVIN LEE MANHEIM

ABSTRACT

We describe the process of solving a highway location problem
as the application in sequence of one or more operators. Each
operator has two basic components: SEARCH, the activity in which
alternative actions are generated; and SELECTION, the activity in
which a choice is made among the generated actions. These operators differ with respect to their costs, the information about
solutions they provide, and their "levels": the precision with
which they specify solutions.

We define level in the following way: Each operator generates
actions of a characteristic kind. For example, in highway location
we have operators which produce bands of interest, alignments, profiles, etc. The actions produced by one operator can be compared
with those produced by another operator: we say that action A
includes action B if action A can be interpreted as a set of actions
like B. If the actions produced by operator N characteristically
are included in actions produced by operator M, then we say that
operator M is of higher level than operator N. The level relation
yields an ordering over the set of operators available to the
engineer.

Given a number of operators, in general there is only one
which produces actions which can be considered to be solutions to
the particular problem. This is the lowest-level operator in the
set; we call the actions produced by this operator elemental
actions. We assume that the cost of an elemental action is determined with certainty by the selection part of that operator.

Actions produced by any other operators can be interpreted as
sets of elemental actions. We call these non-elemental actions.
One particular non-elemental action is the universal action, or
set of all elemental actions.

An experiment is defined as the application of an operator to an action which was produced previously (or the universal action) to yield another action. The new action is of lower level than the action from which it was produced, and included in it. A highway location process can be described as the execution of a series of such experiments.

Each time the engineer executes an experiment he incurs a cost. The action resulting from an experiment, and its cost, is uncertain. Our objective is to determine, at any point in the location process, which experiment is the best one to do next, considering the possible results of the experiment and the cost of executing it.

We have developed a model to be used to determine the best experiment to do next. This model uses Bayesian decision theory. We assume that the engineer can place a subjective probability distribution over each non-elemental action which he has generated previously; this functions as a "prior" distribution. We also assume that each operator is characterized by a conditional probability distribution. For a given experiment, the probability distribution over the possible costs of the action produced is obtained from the prior over the action to which the operator is to be applied, and the conditional distribution for that operator. The observed result of the experiment is the cost of the action produced; given this result, the prior distributions over one or more non-elemental actions (chosen according to certain rules) are revised according to Bayes Theorem.

If the operator used was the one of lowest level, then the action produced is elemental, and a possible solution to the problem. If some other operator was used, then the action produced is non-elemental; no solution has been gained, but possibly the engineer has improved his prospects of ultimately obtaining a solution.

In choosing among possible experiments to do next, the objective is to balance the cost of doing an experiment against the returns, as reflected in terms of getting solutions less costly than the best found so far. With the probabilistic model described, an expected-value criterion is used to determine the best experiment.

The computations required to actually determine the best experiment are performed by computer. The program utilizes several simple heuristics to do this computation, and has been implemented and run on the M.I.T. Compatible Time Sharing System (IBM 7094).

An example computation for a hypothetical location process is given, as well as several examples of other types of analyses which utilize this model. We conclude with a discussion of the implications of this research for the design of a man-machine system for highway location.

Thesis Supervisor: Aaron Fleisher
Title: Associate Professor of Urban and Regional Studies

Acknowledgments

The research reported in this document was made possible through the support extended to the Civil Engineering Systems Laboratory by the Massachusetts Department of Public Works and the U.S. Bureau of Public Roads (Agreement 1438); and through the award of a Stouffer Fellowship to the author by the Joint Center for Urban Studies of M.I.T. and Harvard University. The author also acknowledges the support of the M.I.T. Computation Center and of Project MAC for computational facilities, especially the time-sharing system.

The author wishes to express his deep gratitude to Professor Aaron Fleisher, Department of City and Regional Planning, who gave so very much of his energies and time to supervision of this thesis; to Professor Charles L. Miller, director of the Systems Laboratory and head, Department of Civil Engineering, for his generous and enthusiastic support of this research; and to Professor Howard Raiffa of the Graduate School of Business, Harvard University, who by his thorough and perceptive reading of the details of the Bayesian decision theory model helped the author over some crucial points in its formulation.

In addition, the author also wishes to thank James E. Burke, for his aid in adapting the program GUIDE I to the time-sharing system; John H. Suhrbier and John V. Robinson for the stimulation of their comments on various drafts; Professor Paul O. Roberts and A. Scheffer Lang for their interest during the formative period of this research; and Thomas Richardson of the Massachusetts Department of Public Works, for his comments on the practice of highway location.

Of course, the author alone is responsible for the content and statement of this research.

The author was extremely fortunate in having Mrs. Barbara Igou to type the several successive drafts and the final manuscript.

No research requiring this much commitment of the author is possible without full support and encouragement from the people most important to him. For her continuing enthusiasm and her willingness to accept the conditions of thesis research, I am most grateful to my wife Andrea.

CONTENTS

LIST OF FIGURES

APPENDICES:

INSIDE BACK COVER:

CHAPTER I
THE HIGHWAY LOCATION PROCESS

The objective of this chapter is to introduce the specific
problem with which we are concerned, highway route location, to
draw from that problem certain aspects of its abstract structure,
and to use those elements to frame the objective of the thesis.

1.   The highway location problem

In this section, we will describe the salient features of a
typical route location problem. First, we will identify those
things about a highway which must be described in order for the
engineer to have solved his location problem. Then we will look
at the objectives which the engineer is trying to achieve by a
highway, both the general economic objective, and the specific
design constraints. Finally, we will describe the simplified
location problem, the "rural" problem, which we have defined in
order not to obscure the mainstream of our discussion by side
issues.[1]

1.1   The specification of a solution

The two termini of a proposed highway are given. The distance between these points is in the range 15-30 miles.

To be considered as a possible solution to this location
problem, the following characteristics of the highway must be
specified:
1.   The location of the centerline of the roadway. This
     is specified in three-dimensional coordinates, refer-
     enced to some state coordinate system.

_____

[1]A good introduction to highway engineering can be found in
Hewes, Laurence I., and Clarkson H. Oglesby, HIGHWAY ENGINEERING,
New York: Wiley and Sons (1954).

a) the two-dimensional coordinates (in the horizontal plane) define the horizontal "alignment" of the roadway.

b) the altitude coordinates define the vertical "profile" of the roadway.

2. The cross-section characteristics of the roadway. Often referred to as the "roadway template," this is a list of specifications of the shape of the roadway: the width each side of the centerline, the slopes from the roadway to the drainage ditches, the depths of the ditches, and the slopes from the edge of the ditches to the existing ground profile (different for cut and for fill conditions).[1] As Figure I-I shows, there may be some thirty or more items which must be specified to describe the desired cross-section of a roadway.[2]

3. Relation to ground surface. The template elements are all characteristics of the roadway, or man-made surface. In addition, certain parameters must be specified to relate this surface to the previously-existing ground surface: for example, the distance from roadway to ground at the centerline and other points in the roadway template, and the distances to right and left of the centerline at which the cut or fill slopes of the

---

[1] The road is in "cut" when it is below the ground surface, not covered as in a tunnel. "Fill" is elevated, on embankment.

[2] This figure shows the input form for a computer program used for estimating the volumes of earthwork required for a particular location. As this form indicates, in practice the template variables are set initially, and then departures from this basic setting are specified explicitly (third section of input form). This figure is taken from the test problem in P.O. Roberts and A. Villaveces, DTM DESIGN SYSTEM, 20K PROGRAM MANUAL, Research Report R62-6, Cambridge, Massachusetts; Civil Engineering Systems Laboratory, M.I.T. (December 1961).

FIGURE I-I TYPICAL TEMPLATE VARIABLES

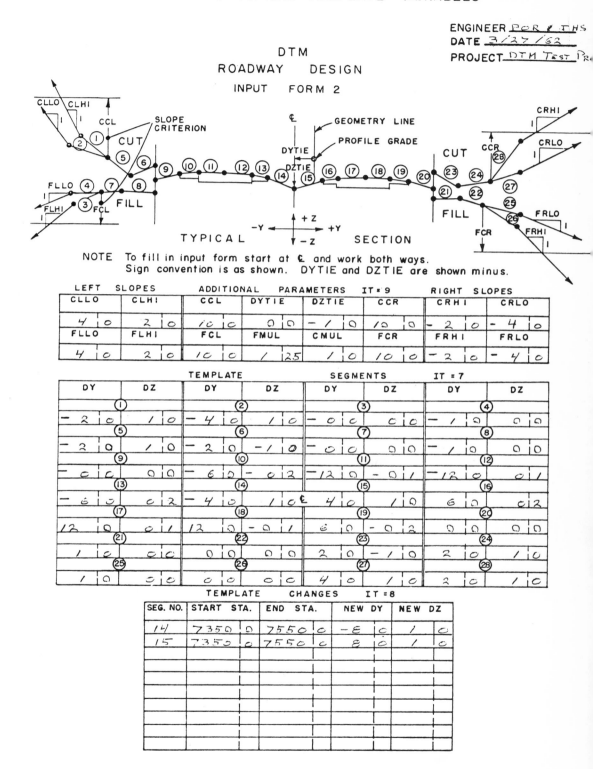

ENGINEER DCR & THS
DATE 3/27/62
PROJECT DTM Test PR

DTM
ROADWAY DESIGN
INPUT FORM 2

TYPICAL SECTION

NOTE To fill in input form start at ℄ and work both ways.
Sign convention is as shown. DYTIE and DZTIE are shown minus.

LEFT SLOPES		ADDITIONAL	PARAMETERS	IT = 9		RIGHT SLOPES	
CLLO	CLHI	CCL	DYTIE	DZTIE	CCR	CRHI	CRLO
4 0	2 0	10 0	0 0	- 1 0	10 0	- 2 0	- 4 0
FLLO	FLHI	FCL	FMUL	CMUL	FCR	FRHI	FRLO
4 0	2 0	10 0	1 25	1 0	10 0	- 2 0	- 4 0

TEMPLATE		SEGMENTS				IT = 7	
DY	DZ	DY	DZ	DY	DZ	DY	DZ
①		②		③		④	
- 2 0	1 0	- 4 0	1 0	- 0 0	0 0	- 1 0	0 0
⑤		⑥		⑦		⑧	
- 2 0	1 0	- 2 0	- 1 0	- 0 0	0 0	- 1 0	0 0
⑨		⑩		⑪		⑫	
- 0 0	0 0	- 6 0	- 0 2	- 12 0	- 0 1	- 12 0	0 1
⑬		⑭		⑮		⑯	
- 6 0	0 2	- 4 0	1 0 ℄	4 0	1 0	6 0	0 2
⑰		⑱		⑲		⑳	
12 0	0 1	12 0	- 0 1	6 0	- 0 2	0 0	0 0
㉑		㉒		㉓		㉔	
1 0	0 0	0 0	0 0	2 0	- 1 0	2 0	1 0
㉕		㉖		㉗		㉘	
1 0	0 0	0 0	0 0	4 0	1 0	2 0	1 0

TEMPLATE	CHANGES		IT = 8		
SEG. NO.	START STA.	END STA.	NEW DY	NEW DZ
14	7350 0	7550 0	- 8 0	1 0
15	7350 0	7550 0	8 0	1 0

man-made surface intersect the natural surface. These can be given directly, or can be interpolated from specification of location, template, and the existing ground surface.[1]

Because a highway has length, all the variables represented by alignment, profile, and template, must be specified at periodic intervals along the highway. In usual practice, these intervals are one hundred feet; the points at which the values of these variables are specified are called "stations."[2]

Finally, there is always a characteristic degree of precision required in the specification of each of these variables. This precision may range from one foot to one-hundredth of a foot in some cases.

From these brief remarks, we see that full specification of the solution to a highway problem may require the specification of the values of a very large number of variables: for example, 30 variables per station, 50 stations per mile, and a length of 20 miles implies some 30,000 variables, whose values must be

----

[1] That is, given the ground surface, the engineer manipulates only alignment, profile and template.

[2] Values may also be specified at intermediate points because of some local peculiarity, such as overpassing another road, etc.

determined by the engineer.

1.2 Objectives in highway location

The provision of transportation is not an intrinsic end
(in general), but is an instrumental one: the purpose of transportation is to aid in the achievement of other goals in society.
These goals generally concern such things as growth of commerce,
provision of accessibility and communication, increasing defensive
ability, etc. Therefore, transportation facilities must be evaluated, ultimately, in terms of the extent to which they achieve
the broader goals of society.

As a practical matter, certain economic criteria are usually
established in an attempt to represent the achievement of these
goals by specific, quantitative indices. Couched in terms of
costs, these criteria generally have three major components:
1. First cost - the resources invested by society in the
    construction of the physical facilities. Specifically,
    these are the costs of land acquisition and of construc-
    tion; construction costs consist of the costs of site
    preparation, earthwork, structures (bridges and drainage),
    and road surface (subgrade and pavement).
2. Continuing costs - the costs borne by society, generally
    by specific public agencies, for the upkeep of the facil-
    ity: administrative costs (e.g. policing) and maintenance
    (snow removal, pavement repairs, etc.).
3. Continuing benefits - these may be indirect or direct.
    Direct benefits are savings in travel costs, time, etc.
    by the actual users of the facility, as compared with
    the previous facility they used (if any). Indirect

benefits are the effects of the transportation facility
on the growth and redistribution of industrial, commercial,
and social activity. It is often assumed that over the
long run the indirect benefits are fully reflected in the
direct benefits, so that only the changes in user costs
are measured to evaluate the benefits.[1] User costs are
composed of:

a) the direct costs of operating the vehicle, generally
   on a per-mile basis - a reflection of wear-and-tear
   on the vehicle, and of fuel and oil consumption.
b) the time costs of travel - the value to the driver
   and passengers of the time they spend in transit.

Once these items are given dollar values, they are combined
into a single cost measure in any one of several ways. The benefit-
cost ratio, and rate-of-return, are often used, but we will use
here the total annual cost.[2] Since the continuing benefits, or
decrease in user costs, can be put on an annual basis, and continuing costs likewise, the first cost of the facility is brought to
an equivalent annual cost basis by the use of present-worth theory.
With the three costs on an annual basis, their sum is the "total
annual cost" of a proposed location: total annual cost = (annual
user costs) + (annual continuing costs) + (first cost on equivalent
annual cost basis).

Choices between locations are made on the basis of this "total
annual cost." That location is chosen for which the total annual

_____
[1] Lang, A.S., and Martin Wohl, "Evaluation of highway impact," in
SOME EVALUATIONS OF HIGHWAY IMPROVEMENT IMPACTS, Bulletin 268,
Washington, D.C.: Highway Research Board (1960). pp. 105-119
[2] Hewes and Oglesby, op.cit., Chapter 4; Morris, William T.,
ENGINEERING ECONOMY, Homewood, Illinois: Richard D. Iruin (1960).

cost is lowest.

It is important to note, however, that as in many other real-world decision problems, there are many important value-dimensions of the location problem which cannot be represented in dollar costs. Specifically, there are a number of constraints which a highway must satisfy, which are rarely expressed in economic terms. Some examples:

   a)   for any desired design speed, there is a minimum accept-
        able radius of curvature of the alignment

   b)   grades must not exceed certain maxima

   c)   the rate of change of grade is also restricted

   d)   there is a minimum acceptable separation between the two
        roadways of a divided highway

   e)   the rate of horizontal curvature, in relation to the
        ground surface and other objects at the roadside must
        allow an adequate field of vision for a certain distance
        along the roadway ("horizontal sight distance")

   f)   vertical clearances, for example under bridges, must meet
        certain minima

   g)   lateral clearances, at bridge supports and in cuts, must
        meet certain minima

   h)   side slopes in cut, or embankment slopes on fill, must
        not exceed certain maxima

There are many others, embodied in several policy manuals.[1]

Costs are never attached to these constraints explicitly, except in rare instances when a decision is made to violate one

[1]American Association of State Highway Officials, A POLICY ON
ARTERIAL HIGHWAYS IN URBAN AREAS. Washington, D.C.:   the
Association (1957).

American Association of State Highway Officials, A POLICY ON
GEOMETRIC DESIGN OF RURAL HIGHWAYS. Washington, D.C.:   the
Association (1954).

of them in order to keep the cost of the highway reasonable. In general, however, these "design standards" are treated as if they were binary-valued variables, all of which must be satisfied for a location to be considered as a possible highway. Then, for those locations for which these many criteria are met, the focus shifts to cost, specifically to the objective of minimizing total annual cost.

1.3 The "rural" location problem

In order to keep the main issues clear, we shall define a prototypical "rural" location problem around which our discussion will center:

a) Land costs are homogeneous throughout the area of possible locations, and are relatively insignificant compared to construction costs.

b) There are no "system" effects - the volume of traffic which will use the facility is essentially independent of the location of the highway within the range of locations being considered.

c) Changes in operating costs are negligible among the possible locations.

d) Continuing costs are negligible.

Although these assumptions are rarely, if ever, met in practice, they allow us to focus primarily upon the construction costs of the locations. Because of previous development work at the M.I.T. Civil Engineering Systems Laboratory,[1] an interesting repertory of computer programs exists for handling earthwork and other aspects

_____

[1] Summarized in Roberts, P.O., and Suhrbier, J.H. HIGHWAY LOCATION ANALYSIS: AN EXAMPLE PROBLEM. Research Report R62-40, Cambridge, Massachusetts: Civil Engineering Systems Laboratory, M.I.T. (1962).

of construction costs.

The general theory and methods which we develop will be as applicable to more realistic problems, as to this "rural" paradigm.

2. A typical highway location process

Most highway location work in the United States is done by state highway departments, or by consultants acting as agents of those departments. It is very instructive to look at the typical way in which route location is being done in these agencies.

In a typical location process, the following activities can be identified:[1]

a) Reconnaissance

Considering a variety of factors, such as general topography, general traffic desires, and political issues, one "band of interest" is generated and picked for further study. A band of interest is an area stretching between the two termini. It may be as wide as several miles, but this will vary significantly with the nature of the terrain.

After reconnaissance, aerial photography is obtained and photogrammetric maps are produced for the selected band of interest.

b) Control points

Sets of constraints on the location are generated and examined for their effects. Known as "control points," these constraints may consist of: the termini of the route, obstacles to be underpassed,

---

[1]This description is based upon conversations with engineers experienced in highway location.

overpassed, or detoured; locations of interchanges
with other routes, etc.

c) Preliminary location

For a set of control points, approximate horizontal
alignments are generated. These are approximate in
that the location of the centerline is not specified
precisely, but to about an accuracy of 200' (where the
right-of-way of the highway may be 150-300'). For
this reason, we can call these approximate alignments
"location bands." Approximate profiles of the ground
surface along these bands may be taken to aid in evaluating them.

Three or four of the best location bands are
selected for further examination.

d) Alignment design

Within the selected location bands, one or more horizontal alignments are generated and evaluated. The
evaluation is on the basis of the ground profile along
the centerline.

e) Roadway design

For alignments which look good, one or more vertical
profiles are generated and evaluated.

The best profile is determined for each alignment.
The three or four best of these locations are selected
for further examination.

f) Interchange studies

For each location, possible layouts for interchanges
with other roads are generated and evaluated.

The single best location, with interchange layouts, is selected.

g) Final design

The single best location, with interchange layouts, is submitted to final design, in which the geometrics of the facility are specified (generated) precisely, and a detailed economic evaluation made (including details of land takings, construction costs, user costs, etc.).

3. The structure of a location process

In this section, we want to abstract from our description of the route location process its basic elements; these elements will then serve as the building blocks of a model of this process.

3.1 Actions

The basic things with which the route location process is concerned are the bands of interest, location bands, alignments, profiles, final designs, etc. As a generic name for these, let us call them "actions." We do not mean to imply by this that there is no difference between location bands, say, and final designs, but rather that there is a certain communality among them.

3.2 Search versus selection

We listed seven major operations, or steps, in the route location process. If we examine them, we will see that in each of these operations two basically different kinds of activities take place. The first kind of activity is the generating of alternative actions. We will call this generation activity SEARCH. The second kind of activity is the choosing of one from among the alternatives which were generated previously. We will call this choosing activity SELECTION.[1]

---

[1] These are not the only kinds of activities which occur in an engineering process. For instance, we might have information acquisition - e.g., acquiring maps or other data - and execution - for example, the actual construction of the highway. We restrict ourselves here to Search and Selection.

To illustrate: in the preliminary location operation, location bands are generated. This is search. The location bands
are also compared, to determine their relative desirabilities;
this is selection. Similarly for reconnaissance and bands of
interest; roadway design and profiles; etc.

3.3 Level

Now, although each of the seven operations *is* alike, in that
both search and selection take place in each, they are different:
reconnaissance *is* different from final design. We describe this
difference by saying that these operators are at different "levels"
of the location process.

Let us explore just what we mean by "level."

The final result of the location process must be a highway
location specified with all the detail necessary for it to be
considered a solution - alignment, profile, and template must
all be specified, and with a certain precision. Let us emphasize
this, by using "location" only to refer to a highway which is
specified with this degree of detail.

But, the only operation in the location process in which
search and selection deal with "locations" is the "final design"
operation. Indeed, if we examine the flow of the location process from reconnaissance through successive operations to final
design, we see that each succeeding operation results in increasing detail and precision of specification. For example, in the
"alignments" operation, only the alignment aspects of location
is specified, while the profile and template remain unspecified.

In the next operation, "profiles," these additional specifications are added, but not yet with sufficient precision for the result to be considered a location.

If we take any two operations, say bands of interest and location bands, we can compare those actions produced by the search part, and evaluated by the selection part of each operation. We compare these actions with respect to the degree of detail and precision with which they are specified: for instance, in the specification of either bands of interest or location bands, neither profile nor template is indicated, but alignment is. The difference is that location bands have alignment (center-line location) specified to about 200', whereas bands of interest may specify alignment to perhaps only two miles.

When we compare two kinds of actions and find that one is characteristically specified with less precision than the other, then we say that the more completely specified action is of lower level than the other. In our example, location bands are of lower level than bands of interest.[1]

3.4 Single-level operators

When we look at our typical location process, we see that each operation consists of both search and selection; further-more, both search and selection are "matched," in that they are concerned with alternatives which are at the same level: search in reconnaissance produces bands of interest, selection in recon-naissance evaluates those bands. All the other search and selec-

[1] An additional interpretation of level is given in Section 3.5.

tion activities in other operations are at different levels. Therefore, we find it convenient to define the idea of a "Single-Level
Operator," or SLO, as consisting of search followed by selection,
both at the same level - that is, dealing with alternatives specified with the same detail and precision.

We shall often use "operator" as a short form of "Single-Level
Operator."

In our typical route location process, there are seven of these
operators.

We can extend the concept of level to operators, as well as
actions. Each SLO is characterized by the detail and precision
with which the actions it produces are specified. Therefore, we
can determine the relative levels of operators by determining
the levels of their characteristic actions.

If we do this for our route location example, we find that the
progression from reconnaissance to final design corresponds to a
progression from higher level to lower level. Bands of interest
are of higher level than control points, which are higher than
location bands, etc. Locations, the product of final design, are
of the lowest level.

3.5 Graphical representation of the history of a location process

It is very instructive to construct a diagrammatic representation of the way the route location process moves from level to level.

Let us look at a simple location process, in which only three
operators are used: reconnaissance, location, and final design.

18

In Figure I-2, we show diagrammatically the history of the solution of a particular location problem, using these operators. In (a), we show the actions which were generated and evaluated, as they might be represented on a map of the topography. The actions are lettered in the order in which they were generated. Two bands of interest were generated, and B was ranked better than A. Within B, two location bands were generated, and D was preferred to C. Finally, within C, one location, E, was generated and evaluated. This was taken as the solution to the location problem.

Recall that the basis for our definition of level was difference in degree of specification of the actions being compared. As this diagram (a) suggests, we can give level another interpretation in highway location.

When we take locations as our basic elements, we find that every other action - band of interest, for example - can be visualized as a collection of locations. If it were practical to enumerate every possible location (in a particular problem), then we could quantify level, by counting the total number of locations included within a typical band of interest, or a typical location band. In this way, we would turn level from an ordering relation to a cardinal measure.

Even though we cannot in fact count total numbers of locations, we use this idea to construct an abstract representation of the location process in terms of sets. This representation is based upon two observations: first, that every action of higher level than a location can be interpreted as a set of locations; second, that the same location belongs to a band of interest as

FIGURE I-2 A HISTORY OF A LOCATION PROCESS

(a)

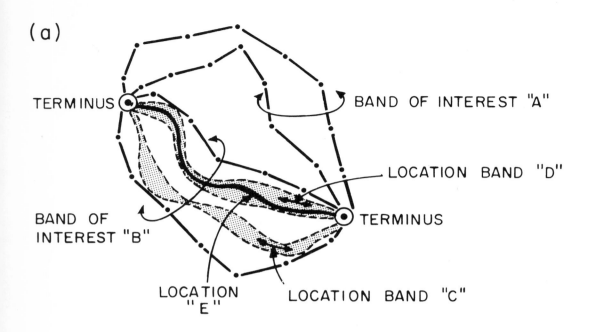

TERMINUS

BAND OF INTEREST "A"

LOCATION BAND "D"

TERMINUS

BAND OF INTEREST "B"

LOCATION "E"

LOCATION BAND "C"

(b)

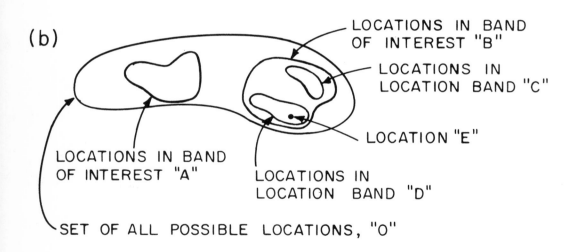

LOCATIONS IN BAND OF INTEREST "B"

LOCATIONS IN LOCATION BAND "C"

LOCATION "E"

LOCATIONS IN BAND OF INTEREST "A"

LOCATIONS IN LOCATION BAND "D"

SET OF ALL POSSIBLE LOCATIONS, "O"

(c)

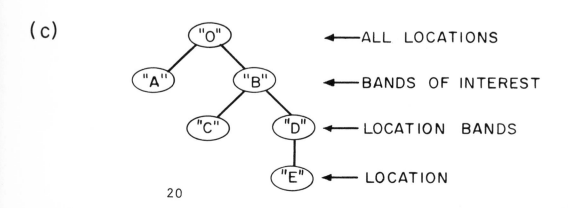

"O" ◄── ALL LOCATIONS

"A" "B" ◄── BANDS OF INTEREST

"C" "D" ◄── LOCATION BANDS

"E" ◄── LOCATION

well as a location band, for example. We show this set representation in diagrammatic form in part (b) of Figure 1-2.

In part (c), we show the relationship of the different actions graphically in a way that emphasizes their levels. First, we show an element to represent the set of all possible locations which might be solutions to the particular problem; this would be obtained by not specifying any characteristic of locations, yielding an action of the very highest level. At the next lower level, we show the two bands of interest, then the location bands at a lower level, and finally the selected location itself, at the lowest level.

The lines between the various actions indicate the way in which one action is obtained from another: for example, the location band C was produced by a search operation on B, a band of interest. When two actions are related in such a way, we will say that the parent action (B, in this case) <u>includes</u> the lower-level action (C here).

The basis for this "inclusion" relationship is evident in part (b) of the figure.

This kind of tree-like diagram summarizes concisely important aspects of the history of a particular route location process. From such a diagram we can determine:
   a)   the number of actions which have been generated and evaluated;
   b)   the sequence in which these actions were produced;
   c)   their relative levels - i.e., by which operators they were produced;
   d)   for each action, its total genealogy - in which actions

it is included, and which actions it includes.
Given a history, we can construct the corresponding diagram;
from a given diagram we can reconstruct these aspects of the
history.

4. The sequence of decisions in a location process

The general question we raise is this: given the past history of a location process, how do we decide what to do next?

To explore the implications of this question, let us examine further the three-operator process of Figure I-2. The possibilities open to us at this particular point (i.e., with location E just generated and evaluated) are:

a) generation and evaluation of locations
    i)   in location band D
    ii)   in location band C
    iii)   in band of interest B but not in the location bands C or D
    iv)   in band of interest A
    v)   not in bands of interest A or B
b) generation and evaluation of location bands
    i)   in band of interest B
    ii)   in band of interest A
    iii)   not in either band of interest
c) generation and evaluation of bands of interest
    i)   only one possibility - not in either band of interest
d) termination of the process.

Execution of any one of these options will result in the addition of a new action to the "tree" of actions. We show each of these possibilities in Figure I-3. Thus, we see that as the location process evolves, the tree diagram will change to reflect the actual history of the location process.

This diagram is important because it emphasizes that the decision which the engineer has to make is not only about which operator

23

to use, but also on which action he should operate to produce a new action. Only if both operator and action are specified do we know where in the tree to place the new action.

This kind of decision must be made many times in a location process, until finally the decision is made to terminate. These are the decisions which lead us to describe route location as a sequential decision process: each time that an operator is used to produce a new action, a decision must be made about what to do next - which operator, on which action.

Because of the multi-level nature of the route location problem,[1] we must distinguish this as a "hierarchically-structured" sequential decision process. The term "hierarchical" arises from the basic diagram expressing the relationships among the actions. Because this diagram is so useful in summarizing the history of a hierarchically-structured location process, we shall often refer to the diagram itself as "the hierarchical structure" of a particular process.

_____
[1] Of course, the location problem is only one of a large class of problems with this same characteristic.

FIGURE I-3 POSSIBLE NEW ACTIONS

PRESENT TREE:

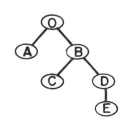

NEW ACTIONS:

(a,i)

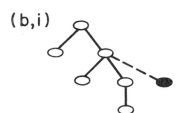

(a,ii)

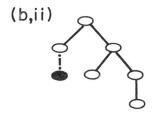

(a,iii)

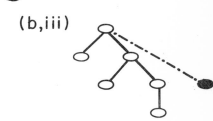

(a,iv)

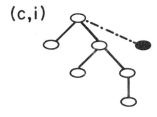

(a,v)

(b,i)

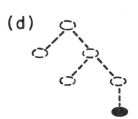

(b,ii)

(b,iii)

(c,i)

(d)

TREE SHOWING
ALL ABOVE
POSSIBILITIES

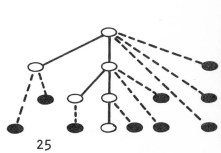

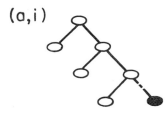
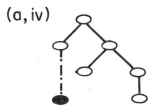
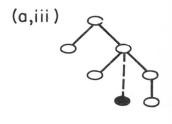
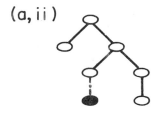
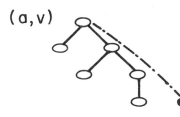
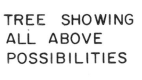

25

5. Objective of this thesis

From our analysis of the location process, we have identified a series of decisions which the engineer must make. The objective of this thesis is the formulation of a rational procedure for the engineer to use in making these decisions.

We present such a procedure in Chapter II. The essential characteristics of this procedure are:

1. The basic choices are among combinations, where a combination consists of an operator, and the action to which the operator is to be applied. We call these combinations experiments.

2. Only locations which meet the design standards are potential solutions. Therefore, the value of other actions at higher levels - e.g., location bands - is only in the likelihood that they contain desirable locations.

3. The engineer incurs a fixed cost every time he executes an experiment. Therefore, the possibility of getting a location which costs less than the best found so far must be balanced against the cost of the experiment.

4. The judgements of the engineer are expressed in the form of probability distributions over the results of possible experiments.

5. With these probabilities, and the utility functions defined by the costs of the experiments and the costs of the locations produced, Bayesian decision theory is used to compute the expected return for each possible experiment. The engineer then executes that experiment with the maximum expected return. (The experiments considered include terminating the location process.)

In Chapter III, we describe the way we have implemented this
model, in the form of a computer program, and we illustrate the
use of the model with several examples. The first example is a
history of a hypothetical location process; this history is summarized in Chart A (inside back cover). Two other examples
indicate various explorations which can be made in the context
of any particular location problem.

Chapter IV begins with summary of the model. We then discuss
a number of the assumptions of the model, its implications, and
major directions for extending this research. We conclude with
a discussion of some of the implications of this work for the
design of an integrated man-machine system for highway route location.

CHAPTER II

A BAYESIAN DECISION THEORY MODEL OF A

HIERARCHICALLY STRUCTURED SEQUENTIAL DECISION PROCESS

1. Objectives

The objective of a problem-solving process such as highway location is a solution, described in all the detail necessary for implementation in the real world. The process of trying to find such a solution proceeds by a sequence of "experiments," or operations in which information is acquired about the nature of possible solutions. As a special case, such information may be gained by actually generating a particular solution and determining its cost.

The objective of the model described in this chapter is to provide a rational basis for choosing among the possible sequences of experiments which might be performed in solving a particular problem. We do not attempt to tell the engineer how to find a solution, but how to organize the process by which he will try to find one.

The presentation of this model begins in Section 2 with a description of experiments and level. In Section 3 we describe how we can characterize experiments, with costs and probability distributions.

The subject of the fourth section is the state of the location process: how we describe just where the engineer stands with regard to his objectives. In Section 5, we describe the changes in state that will take place when the engineer executes an experiment and observes its result. This enables us to describe, in Section 6, the nature of the computations necessary for the engineer to determine which experiment he should do next.

Our model is based upon Bayesian decision theory. For the convenience of the reader, we have provided a short description of this theory, and a sample calculation, in Appendix A.

2. Experiments

2.1 Actions

We assume that there is a set of variables sufficiently
complete that any possible solution to the problem at hand can
be described in terms of these variables. In our route location
example, such a set would consist of the variables necessary to
specify the alignment, profile and template, at each station
(100 foot interval) along the highway's centerline.

This set of variables defines a space of all possible solutions to the problem. This can be seen by constructing an n-
dimensional space in which each axis corresponds to one of the
n variables which are needed to describe a solution.

We will call an __action__ any point or set of points in this
space. That is, an action is a solution or set of solutions.

We include in the definition of action what might be called
the "universal" action: the set of all possible solutions. We
also include the "null" action - i.e., no solution, or, more
precisely, finding no solution other than the existing condition.

2.2 Operators

We define a Single-Level Operator (SLO) as a set of procedures which are applied to an action to produce (i) another action
and (ii) an estimate of the cost associated with that action.[1]

_____

[1] In other contexts, where there is not a single measure of utility
this alternate definition may be useful: an SLO produces an
action, and a preference ordering over that action and the previously-generated actions of the same level.

The procedures comprising an operator fall into the following stages:

a) SEARCH is the first stage, being the process in which the new action is generated and identified.

b) SELECTION is the second major stage, being the process in which the newly-generated action is compared with others previously generated, and a statement made about the relative costs of these actions.

Within SELECTION, the following three processes can be identified:

a) PREDICTION is the process in which the effect of the new action on the world is estimated. A fuller title would be, prediction of real-world consequences. In route location, typical examples would be: volume of earth moved, traffic volume, average speed, etc.

b) EVALUATION is the part of selection in which valuations are placed on the consequences. Typical valuations in route location are hours of driver time, dollars of construction cost, etc.

c) DECISION is the final part of selection, in which the relative desirability of the action is determined, relative to previously-generated actions, on the basis of the valuations of the consequences. In decision, value conflicts are reconciled, as also issues of uncertainty.[1]

These procedures which form operators are, in the every day meaning, "actions," in that they involve "doing something." The purpose of distinguishing actions from operations is to separate the actions which are solutions to the problem (locations, e.g.)

---

[1] In the route location problem as we have defined it - the "rural" paradigm - we have assumed that there is no uncertainty, and that dollars are the sole measures of value. Therefore, decision is trivial, involving simply the comparison of total annual costs, and evaluation involves the placing of dollar values on each of the physical consequences.

from the "actions" of finding those solutions, or what we have called the processes of search and selection.

2.3 Discrimination, inclusion, and level

The basic idea of level is the difference between the preliminary, or planning, stage and the final design stage of an engineering process. In our example of a typical route location process, there were seven levels, ranging from reconnaissance through final design. The objective of this section is to give a precise meaning to the idea of level.

We can consider the selection component of any Single-Level Operator as a mapping from the space of actions to the line representing the set of all possible costs. That is, given the coordinates of a point or set of points in the action-space, selection gives us the cost of the corresponding action.

Let us take some particular selection procedure, and start applying it to the points which are near a given action in the action-space. For each point we determine the cost of the corresponding action: how much different do these actions have to be before we can detect a difference in their costs? Put another way, what is the ability of that particular selection scheme to distinguish among the actions?

Every selection procedure is characterized by its ability to discriminate among actions in the action space. Let us emphasize this by defining the concept of a _metric:_ the metric of an SLO is a division of the action space into sets of actions such that the selection component of the SLO can distinguish between two actions if they are from different sets, but cannot distinguish between actions from the same set. A metric is a set of exhaustive disjoint subsets of the set of points in the action space.

The metrics corresponding to two SLO's can be compared, leading to the concept of _inclusion_: metric A _includes_ metric B if and only if every action (i.e., set of points in action space) defined by metric A contains

i)   all the points contained in _at least one_ action defined by metric B, and

ii)   points from _more than one_ action defined by metric B.

We illustrate this in Figure II-1. In part (a), we show the n-dimensional action space defined by the set of variables necessary in describing fully a solution. In part (b), we have taken all the points in this space and arrayed them in the plane (using some unspecified set of procedures). In part (c) we show two metrics, and in part (d) we show how overlaying the two illustrates that metric A does include metric B.

The notion of inclusion as we have defined it is very close to the conventional notion of set inclusion.[1] We emphasize this by using the symbol $\supset$ to denote inclusion, as: A $\supset$ B for "A includes B." Between any two metrics A and B there are three

---

[1] For example, Mood, Alexander M., and Franklin A. Graybill, INTRODUCTION TO THE THEORY OF STATISTICS. New York: McGraw-Hill p.14, (1963), or any elementary text on set theory. Inclusion in set theory is a relation between sets: set A includes set B if and only if every element of B is also an element of A. Our notion of metric inclusion is a relation between sets of sets, since each metric is a set of exhaustive disjoint subsets of the set of solutions; and the stipulated conditions are much stronger than ordinary set inclusion.

FIGURE II−1 METRICS AND INCLUSION

(a) ACTION SPACE

(b) ALTERNATIVE REPRESENTATION

SPACE OF ALL
POSSIBLE ACTION

(c) TWO METRICS

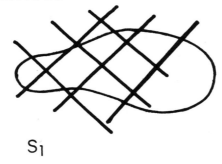

S_1 S_2

(d) INCLUSION

$S_1 \supset S_2$

NOTE: RECTANGULAR GRIDS ARE USED TO REPRESENT
METRICS FOR GRAPHIC CLARITY ONLY.

possibilities for the inclusion relationship:

a)   A $\supset$ B

b)   B $\subset$ A

c)   no inclusion relationship exists between the corresponding metrics.

Note that inclusion is transitive. That is, for three metrics A, B, C, if A $\supset$ B and B $\supset$ C, then A $\supset$ C.

Since every SLO has a characteristic metric, the inclusion relationship between metrics leads to a parallel relationship between operators, which we call <u>level</u>:

operator A is of higher level than operator B if and only if the metric for A includes the metric for B.

Just as there are three possibilities for the inclusion relation, so there are three possibilities for level:

a)   A is of higher level than B

b)   B is of higher level than A

c)   the level relation is not defined between the two operators.

The level relation, like inclusion, is transitive.

For any finite set of operators, statements can be made about the level relationship between every possible pair of operators. Since level is an ordering relationship, we can represent these statements by an arrow diagram, as in Figure II-2. If level is defined between all pairs of operators, then we obtain the "linear" form shown in part (b) where we have used the transitivity property to eliminate "redundant" statements of level. In the sequel, we shall restrict our discussion to problems where level is defined between all pairs of operators, and so such "linear" diagrams can be constructed. Most of what we say is easily extendible to problems where this condition does not hold, as in part (a) of this figure.

In the route location example, the meaning of level as a comparison between metrics is very clear, because of the geometrical nature of the problem. For example, the metric corresponding to the bands of interest operator includes the metric corresponding to final design, because every band of interest contains a large number of locations. In this case, the phenomenon which takes place is aggregation: many locations aggregate to form a single band of interest.

The foregoing argument and definitions justify the image given in Section 3.5 of Chapter I, in which the representation of level by sets and subsets was suggested. However, the first description of level we gave was in terms of relative degree of completeness and precision in the specification of actions (Section I-3.3). This is also equivalent to the definition in terms of metrics; for, if more precision is required in the specification of actions, then a finer distinction is made among the points in the action space, and a finer metric is imposed; while if some additional aspect of an action is specified, then what was formerly one action is now differentiated into a number of actions by the possible values of this new variable. So we see that all our definitions of level are consistent, and just different visualizations of the same phenomenon.

Finally, we note that inclusion has been defined as a relation between metrics, and level as a relation between operators. Both these concepts can be extended to actions themselves:

FIGURE II-2 LEVEL RELATIONSHIPS

(a)   4 OPERATORS: A, B, C, D

METRICS: S_A, S_B, S_C, S_D

INCLUSIONS:

$S_A \supset S_B$ $\qquad\qquad$ $S_C \supset S_A$

$S_B \supset S_D$ $\qquad\qquad$ $S_C \supset S_B$

$S_C \supset S_D$

ARROW DIAGRAM:

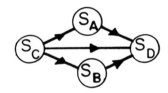

(b)   INCLUSIONS:

$S_A \supset S_D$ $\qquad\qquad$ $S_C \supset S_A$

$S_B \supset S_D$ $\qquad\qquad$ $S_C \supset S_B$

$S_C \supset S_D$ $\qquad\qquad$ $S_A \supset S_B$

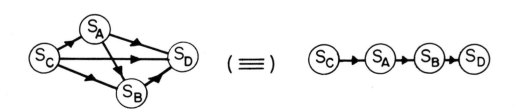

i)   Action A <u>includes</u> action B whenever every point in the
action space in B is also in A. (This is the straight
set-theoretic definition of inclusion.)

ii) Action A is of <u>higher level</u> than action B whenever A
includes B.

2.4 Elemental and non-elemental actions

Given a set of operators which may be used to solve a particular problem, we shall assume that there is one operator which is
of lower level than any other operator. We shall call this the
<u>elemental operator</u> and will call the actions which it produces
<u>elemental actions</u>. In contrast, actions produced by any operators
of higher level we will call <u>non-elemental actions</u>.

The significance of this distinction is that the elemental
operator represents the greatest power we have to distinguish
among possible solutions to the problem. If two points in the
action space are indistinguishable by the elemental operator, then
for all practical purposes they are the same action, because they
have the same cost.

In the route location example, only the products of final
design, locations, are elemental actions. All other actions -
bands of interest, location bands, alignments, profiles, etc. -
are non-elemental actions.

As a consequence of defining the elemental operator as the
operator of lowest level, and of the definitions of level and
inclusion, we know that any non-elemental action includes locations from more than one elemental action. All the locations

included within an elemental action have the same cost (because
they are indistinguishable); locations from different elemental
actions will have different costs. Therefore, a non-elemental
action does not have a single cost, but a distribution; this
distribution represents the frequency distribution of locations
from different elemental actions.

For example, each location generated in final design can
have a precise cost (determined by using the selection part of
the elemental operator on that location). A band of interest,
however, does not have a single cost, but a distribution of costs,
corresponding to the distribution of costs of the set of locations which are included in that band.

If a non-elemental action does not have a single cost, what
then is the significance of the single number which is output
from the application of a non-elemental operator? For example,
a band operator outputs a "cost" for the band of interest which
it has generated.

To explain this, we note that although the costs corresponding to a non-elemental action have a distribution, we could try
to represent that distribution by some parameter: for example,
the mean of the distribution, variance, median, mode, minimum
value, lowest decile value, etc. Conceptually, we can visualize
the selection component of a non-elemental operator as yielding
the value of some such parameter.

Regardless of the exact relationship of this parameter to
the distribution, we shall keep our language simple by referring
to the output of selection as a "cost."

2.5 Precise definition of experiment

We are now prepared to define precisely what we mean by an experiment:

> An experiment e_{ij} consists of the application of a Single-Level Operator i, to the non-elemental action j. The results of an experiment are a new action and a cost associated with that action. If the action produced is elemental, the cost is the cost of the action. If the action is non-elemental, then the "cost" is some parameter of the distribution of costs of those elemental actions included within that non-elemental action.

Note that although the product of an experiment may be an elemental or non-elemental action, an experiment can be performed only on a non-elemental action.

The information produced by the experiment is carried in the cost associated with the new action by the selection part of the operator. Since only an elemental action can be a solution, the value of a non-elemental action lies only in this information about the elemental actions included within it.

3. Characterization of an experiment

3.1 The cost of an experiment

We will assume that the cost of an experiment e_{ij} is known with certainty, is constant from experiment to experiment, and is dependent upon the operator only. We will represent this cost by c_i.

3.2 Probabilistic characterization of the outcome of an experiment

In the experiment e_{ij}, operator i is applied to action j to produce another action, k, and a statement of the cost, y, of that new action. Let $P_{ij}(y)$ express the probability that experiment e_{ij} produces an action with cost y.

We will assume that $P_{ij}(y)$ can be computed from two probability distributions $f_j(\theta)$ and $g_i(y|\theta)$ such that:

a) $f_j(\theta)$ is a property of the action j only (consider θ for the moment as a dummy argument);

b) $g_i(y|\theta)$ is a characteristic of the operator i only;[1]

c) $P_{ij}(y) \equiv \int g_i(y|\theta) \, f_j(\theta) \, d\theta$

We will define these distributions more fully in the following sections.

3.3 Characterizing an action with a prior

We have noted (Section 2.4) that for each non-elemental action there is some distribution of the costs of all the included elemental actions. Now, the engineer is not interested so much in this

---

[1] $g_i(y|\theta)$ is a conditional probability, read as "the probability of y, given θ."

"true" distribution, as he is in the distribution of what he would get if he were to apply the elemental SLO to this non-elemental action. In our example, for instance, the engineer is not really interested in the distribution of costs of all possible locations included within a particular band of interest; but he _is_ interested in the costs of those locations he will get, as a result of his search activities, on the next one, ten, or one hundred applications of the elemental SLO.

In general, the distribution over the output of the elemental SLO will be different from the true distribution of costs, for any particular non-elemental action. The true distribution represents a purely random draw of a location from the band; on the other hand, the search activity involved in applying the SLO is purposive, in that the engineer is deliberately trying to get a location with as low a cost as possible.

Clearly, the engineer does not really have (at present) any way of determining directly either of these distributions. Rather, what he must do is estimate some distribution of this kind which he is willing to use as a basis for his decisions.

We shall define such a subjective distribution in the following way:

> For a particular non-elemental action j, assume
> that the elemental operator is applied some large
> number of times n.[1] The frequency distribution

---

[1] The number n is subject only to the constraint that it be enough greater than any reasonably-likely number of operator applications so that one never actually gets a specific value of θ. That is, the purpose of θ is to serve as a reference point which is never actually attained.

of the costs of the n elemental actions is denoted
by some distribution h(c), where c = cost. Let θ
be some parameter of this distribution (mean, variance, median, mode, lowest quartile, decile; least
of the n costs, etc.). We ask the engineer to give
us his judgement as to the relative likelihood of
different values of θ; we represent this judgement as $f_j(\theta)$.

We assume that the engineer has a distribution $f_j(\theta)$ for every
action j which he has produced so far (in a particular location
process). The purpose of these distributions is to express the
information which the engineer acquires as he executes experiments
in the location process. Each time he obtains a new action and
its associated cost, he acquires information about the true distribution of costs of the locations included within various non-elemental actions. This information is expressed in changes in his
subjective estimate of the chances of different outcomes from
future applications of the elemental SLO.

For example, if θ represents the cost of the cheapest of the
n locations, then each time the engineer obtains a cost estimate
for some band of interest, location band, or other non-elemental
action, his judgement about the chances of getting different values
of this cost will change. An estimate higher than he expected will
generally cause him to believe higher values of θ to be more likely
than lower values.[1]

_____
[1] The exact rules which express the way in which the distributions
$f_j(\theta)$ change are discussed in Section 5.3 below.

We need some way of representing the engineer's information because his choice of an experiment must be based on this information. A subjective probability distribution like $f_j(\theta)$ is one possible representation.

3.4 Characterizing the operators with conditionals

We will characterize each Single-Level Operator i with a conditional probability distribution $g_i(y|\theta)$, defined thus:

> Given that some action j is characterized by a particular value of the parameter θ, say θ_o, $g_i(y|\theta_o)$ is the probability that application of operator i to that action will produce an action with cost equal to y.

As indicated above, the engineer's information will be changed by his observing the result of an experiment. Since we will represent his information at any particular time by prior distributions $f_j(\theta)$, we need some way of changing these distributions to correspond to the change in the engineer's information when he observes the result of an experiment. The distributions $g_i(y|\theta)$ will provide a way of doing this.[1]

3.5 Obtaining the data

We assume that determining the costs per application of an operator, c_i, is not difficult. Our major interest in this section is with obtaining the prior probability distributions $f_j(\theta)$ and the conditional distributions $g_i(y|\theta)$.

---

[1] Cf. Section 5.3.

The priors and conditionals can be estimated directly by the engineer, if he wishes. The method which we outline here is indirect, but we think most engineers will find it useful, particularly in the first stages of their use of this model.

Although the details which follow are not used in the sequel, we present them here to counter any objection about the difficulty of estimating $g(y|\theta)$ directly.

1. For some experiment e_{ij} we ask the engineer for the following information (prior to his execution of that experiment):

    a) $P_{ij}(y)$, his estimate of the likelihood of the different costs y

    b) $P_{ij}(\theta|y)$, his distribution over θ, conditional upon having observed that the action produced does have a cost y. We obtain this distribution for each possible result y.[1]

2. From this data, the following quantities are then computed:

    a) the joint distribution,

$$P_{ij}(\theta,y) = P_{ij}(y)\, P_{ij}(\theta|y)$$

    b) a prior,

$$f_j(\theta) = \int P_{ij}(\theta,y)\ dy$$

    c) a conditional,

$$g_i(y|\theta) = \frac{P_{ij}(\theta,y)}{f_j(\theta)}, \quad \text{for each } \theta.$$

---

[1] In actual operation of GUIDE 1, our computer program, the engineer may submit this distribution for as many results y as he cares to. We adjust the following calculations accordingly.

48

3. Steps 1 and 2 are repeated for at least as many experiments e_{ij} as necessary to get a distribution $f_j(\theta)$ for each action j, and a conditional distribution $g_i(y|\theta)$ for each operator i.

a) If experiments e_{ij} are picked such that more than one estimate is obtained for some particular prior and/or conditional, then the arithmetic average of these estimates is used.

b) If a previous estimate for any of these distributions is available, as for example the distribution used in a previous computation, then this is averaged in with the new estimates. All the new estimates and the older one are weighted equally.

c) A prior $f_j(\theta)$, once computed, may be assigned to more than one action j, if the engineer considers that his information is the same for several actions.

4. For computational speed and simplicity, it is assumed that $g_i(y|\theta)$ can be represented as a function $w_i(y-\theta)$. Each computed conditional $g_i(y|\theta)$ can easily be written in the form $v_i(m|\theta)$, where $m = y-\theta$. However, in general this function of m will be different for different θ's. Therefore, we obtain $w_i(y-\theta)$ as a weighted average of the functions $v_i(m|\theta)$, using $f_j(\theta)$ as a weighting function:

We have

$$g_i(y|\theta) = \frac{P_{ij}(\theta,y)}{f_j(\theta)}$$

Let $m \equiv y-\theta$. Then,

$$v_i(m|\theta) \equiv g_i(\theta+m|\theta)$$

$$v_i(m|\theta) = \frac{P_{ij}(\theta, \ \theta+m)}{f_j(\theta)}$$

Defining $w_i(y-\theta)$ as a weighted average, we have

$$w_i(m) = \sum_\theta f_j(\theta) \cdot v_i(m|\theta)$$

$$= \sum_\theta P_{ij}(\theta, \ \theta+m).$$

This relates the desired SLO characteristic to the input data.

A sample computation is indicated in Figure II-3.

The discussion in this section indicates two critical assumptions of the model:

a)   independence of the prior and the conditional;

b)   form of the conditional as $g(y-\theta)$.

FIGURE II-3 SAMPLE INPUT DATA AND COMPUTATIONS

a) θ, y measured in units of $\$1000$.

b) for experiment $(i,j) = (1,000)$: We first obtain $P_{ij}(y)$, the engineer's judgement of the probability of result y —

y	$P_{ij}(y)$
1	0
2	0
3	0
4	.2
5	.5
6	.3
7	0
	1.0

c) we then ask the engineer, given the result y, what his posterior would be over θ:

observed y	posterior distribution θ	$f_j''(\theta/y)$
4	3	.1
	4	.6
	5	.3
		1.0
5	4	.3
	5	.5
	6	.2
		1.0
6	4	.1
	5	.4
	6	.5
		1.0

FIGURE II-3 (continued)

	θ:3	4	5	6	P(y)
y: 4	.1	.6	.3	0	.2
5	0	.3	.5	.2	.5
6	0	.1	.4	.5	.3

d) we then compute the joint distribution $P(\theta,y)$ and its marginal $P(\theta)$:

	θ: 3	4	5	6
y: 3	0	0	0	0
4	.02	.12	.06	0
5	0	.15	.25	.10
6	0	.03	.12	.15
P(θ):	.02	.30	.43	.25

e) from this we compute:

$$g_i(m) = \sum_\theta P(\theta, y = m + \theta)$$

$P(\theta, y = m + \theta)$:

	θ:3	4	5	6	g(m)
m: −1	0	0	.06	.10	.16
0	0	.12	.25	.15	.52
+1	.02	.15	.12	0	.29
+2	0	.03	0	0	.03

f) $g_i(m)$ would be used as the likelihood $g(y/\theta)$ for operator i ; $P(\theta)$ as the prior $f_j(\theta)$ for action j ; except that if other estimates are made, the average $\bar{g}_i(m)$ is computed. For example, two estimates for $g_i(m)$:

FIGURE II - 3 (continued)

	(1) $g_i(m)$	(2) $g_i(m)$	$\bar{g}_i(m)$
m: −2	.05	.06	.055
−1	.08	.22	.15
0	.42	.39	.405
+1	.30	.26	.28
+2	.15	.07	.11

4.   Describing the state of the process

4.1   Basic state variables

As experiments are executed and their results observed, the status of the route location process changes. Since the process proceeds by generating and evaluating actions, the status is described fully by the list of actions which have been produced so far, together with the following characteristics of each:

1. Sequence number: this gives the order in which the action was generated. In general, the action with sequence number 1 is the set of all possible actions, the "universal" action. Sequence numbers are assigned in sequence, as the actions are generated.

2. Level: the level of the action.

3. A label, representing the genealogy of the action - in which action(s) of higher level it is included. This will be described fully in the following section, 4.2.

4. Cost distributions:[1]
   a)   If the action is elemental, then there is a specific cost associated with it.[2]
   b)   If the action is not elemental, then there is a distribution of costs associated with it.

5. The value of the least-cost of the elemental actions found so far:
   a)   This is somewhat redundant as a variable, in that it can be found by examination of the list of actions and their characteristics, but it is so important in describing the state of the process that we distinguish it.

---

[1] Cf. Section 3.3.

[2] We assume no uncertainty, in order to keep our discussion simple. Appropriate extension to incorporate uncertainty via a probability distribution would be straight forward.

b) If no elemental action has been generated yet, then
    this value is taken to be the cost of not solving
    the location problem - i.e., the value of the "null"
    action.

c) Since we use cost as our primary criterion, and
    assume that all locations satisfy any other constraints
    finding the least cost of several elemental actions
    is trivial (under certainty).

Note that, once determined, the sequence number, level, and label
are fixed properties of the actions and cannot change.

4.2 Labelling scheme for actions

It is desirable to keep track of the inclusion relationships
among the actions generated so far.[1] The tree-like diagram in
Figure I-2 is one way of representing these; however, it is desirable to supplement this graphic representation with a notation
which will also uniquely identify the past history of an action,
as expressed by inclusion relationships.

The following rules define such a notation:

1. If N is the number of SLO's available to the engineer,
    then each action is described by a label consisting of
    N characters.

2. Each character consists of one or more digits.

3. The total action domain has a label consisting of N zeros.

4. Number the SLO's down from the top of the tree: SLO N
    produces the elemental actions, SLO I the highest-level
    actions. An action produced by SLO m has identifying
    characters in the first m positions of its label; and
    zeros in all the last (N - m) positions.

_____ ___

[1] These are particularly necessary in updating the probability
distributions. Cf. Section 5.3.

5. If an action produced by SLO m is included in an action produced by SLO i, then the left-most i characters of both labels are identical.

6. Let A be an action produced by SLO i. Consider SLO m, with m greater than i. (SLO i is higher level than SLO m.) Every action produced by SLO m which is included in A has the same left-most (m-1) characters as A, but differs in the characters in the mth position: the first action produced by SLO m from A has a 1 in this position, the second has a 2, etc.

Although these rules are difficult to describe clearly and to implement in the computer, their implications for a labelling system are actually fairly simple, and best illustrated by example. In Figure 11-4, we illustrate this labelling system by applying it to a three-SLO example.

As this figure shows, from the label associated with each action can be determined:

1. its level;
2. its antecedents, those actions of higher level in which it is included;
3. the order in which it was generated, among those actions of the same level with the identical antecedents.

These are found as follows:

1. count the number of consecutive right-most characters which are all zeroes, and denote this by k;
2. the level of the action, m = k + 1;
3. the order in which this action was generated, among those actions at level m with the same antecedents, is given by the value of the character in the mth position (counting from the left; this is also the first non-zero position when counting from the right);

56

4. the antecedents of this action are all those other actions of higher level (more than k right-most zero characters), for which all the significant (i.e., left-most, non-zero) characters are the same as the corresponding ones in the label for this action.

FIGURE II-4 THE LABELLING SCHEME

(a) THREE OPERATORS: THEREFORE, EACH LABEL HAS THREE CHARACTERS

(b) INCLUSION RELATIONSHIPS:

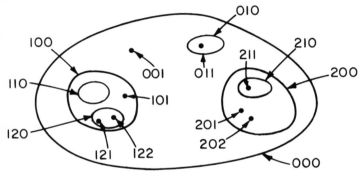

(c) TREE:

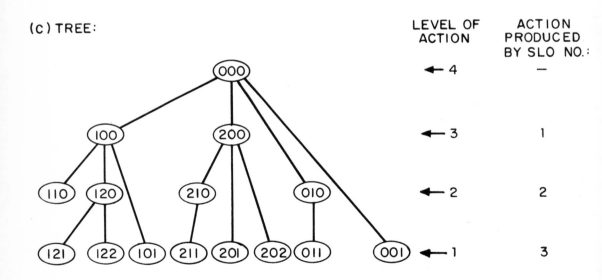

LEVEL OF ACTION   ACTION PRODUCED BY SLO NO.:

←4   —

←3   1

←2   2

←1   3

5. Updating the state of the process

5.1 General

After a particular experiment is executed and the engineer observes the result, the status of the process is different from what it was before the execution of the experiment. The change in status is reflected in three ways: there is (potentially) a reduction in the cost of the least-expensive location found so far; there is a new action to be added to the list of actions; certain characteristics of the previously-generated actions change:

a) The experiment can result in a reduction in the cost of the lowest-cost elemental action found so far only if:
  i) the action produced was elemental - i.e., the elemental operator was used; <u>and</u>
  ii) the cost of the action produced was lower than the cost of the lowest-cost elemental action found previously.

  If both these conditions obtain, then this aspect of the state of the process is revised accordingly, by setting this variable equal to the cost of the new elemental action.

b) In order to add the new action to the list of actions, we need its sequence number, level, and label, and a probability distribution $f(\theta)$:
  i) The sequence number is one more than the number of actions previously generated.
  ii) The level is equal to the level of the SLO used to generate and evaluate the action.

iii) The label is computed, as a function of the labels of all the other actions which had previously been generated, according to the procedure described in Section 5.2, below.

iv) The probability distribution is computed according to the rules indicated in Section 5.3, below.

c) The sequence number, level, and label, of the actions which had existed previously to the execution of the last experiment are permanent characteristics of those actions. Therefore, only the probability characteristic can potentially change. The rules for computing these changes are given in Section 5.3, below.

5.2 Labelling the new action

We shall first introduce a compact notation for identifying an experiment.

To identify the SLO's available, we will use Roman numerals, numbering them in order of <u>decreasing</u> level. That is, if there are three SLO's, actions at the most precise level, level one, are produced by SLO III, while the highest-level operator, SLO I, produces actions at level 3. (Level 4 is the total action domain, the "universal" action.)

To identify the actions, we use their labels. Thus, in a three-SLO situation, we use (000) to denote the total action domain; all other actions would have similar three-character labels.

To completely describe an experiment, then, we can use an ordered pair such as:

```
(I; 000)    =   SLO I applied to the total action domain (000)
(III; 030) =   SLO III applied to action 030 (of level 2,
                   produced by SLO II)
(III; 200) =   SLO III applied to action 200 (of level 3,
                   produced by SLO I)
```

As an example, we shall look at a particular stage in a three-operator process. These are the actions generated so far:

ID	Label
1	000
2	100
3	110
4	001
5	010
6	200
7	201

The execution of any one of the following experiments would result in the generation of one additional action, with the indicated label:

Experiment	Action Produced
(I; 000)	(300)
(II; 000)	(020)
(II; 100)	(120)
(II; 200)	(210)
(III; 000)	(002)
(III; 100)	(101)
(III; 200)	(202)
(III; 110)	(111)
(III; 010)	(011)

These actions are shown in Figure II-5.

The algorithm for producing a label for the action resulting from an experiment follows from the definition of the labelling scheme:

We call the action on which the SLO was applied the "parent" action, for this experiment. Let N be the number of SLO's available, and let i denote the identification number of that SLO used in the experiment. From our definition of the labelling scheme (Section 4.3), we know the label of the new action must indicate (a) its antecedents, (b) its level, and (c) its order of generation. Therefore, the sequence of operations is thus:

1. set the left-most $(i-1)$ characters of the new label identical to the corresponding characters in the label of the parent action;

2. set the right-most $(N-i)$ characters to zeroes;

3. determine the value of the character in the ith label position (counting from the left) by this procedure:

   a) find all actions in the list (of actions before the execution of the experiment) which meet conditions 1 and 2, i.e., have zeroes in the right-most $(N-i)$ characters, and which have the same left-most $(i-1)$ characters as the parent action;

   b) of these actions find the maximum value of the characters in the ith label position;

   c) the corresponding character in the label for the newly-generated action is one more than this maximum value.

To illustrate, assume that the executed experiment was (111; 200). Then, $i = 3$, and the label of the parent action is (200):

62

FIGURE II-5   LABELLING THE NEW ACTIONS

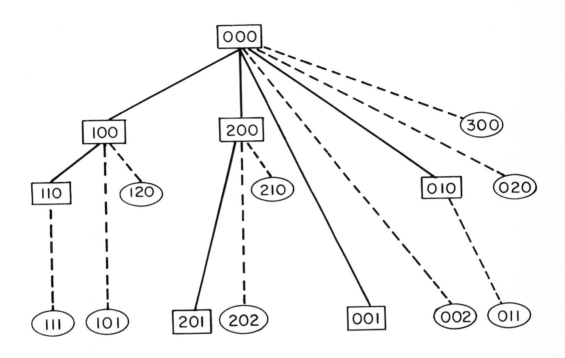

= EXISTING PREVIOUSLY - GENERATED ACTIONS

= POSSIBLE NEW ACTIONS

1. The left-most 2 characters of the new label will be 20.
2. Since N - i = 3 - 3 = 0, the second step has no impact on the label.
3. From the list of actions, we find only one, 201, which has the same antecedents and is the same level. The character in the 3rd position is one, for this action, so the new action will have 2 in this position.
4. Combining these three steps, we get (202) as the label for the new action.

5.3 Changes in the probability distributions

a) Introduction

After the execution of an experiment, the probability distributions for some or all of the previously-generated actions change, and a distribution must be determined for the new action resulting from the experiment. The purpose of this section is to give rules for the required computations. The objective of these rules is to model the changes in the engineer's judgement about the relative success of further investigation, as a result of the information carried by the cost of the new action.

Before going into a detailed exposition of these rules, we shall indicate briefly the key assumptions on which they are based, and illustrate these assumptions.

Let us use again the example of the three-operator process, given in Figure I-2. We have already generated two bands of interest, A and B; two location bands, C and D, included in B; and one location, E, included in D. In addition to these actions, we also

have the action 0, corresponding to the set of all actions.
Assume that we have just completed an experiment involving the
generation of a second location, F, included in D. We have
determined the cost of that location; let this be y^*.

These are our basic assumptions, and their implications
in this example:

1. The experiment e_{ij} produces an action with cost y^*.
    As a result of observing this cost, the engineer's
    prior distribution $f_j(\theta)$ will change. The way this
    distribution changes is given by Bayes Theorem. For
    example, let $f''_D(\theta|y^*)$ denote the distribution after
    the engineer observes that the cost of location E is
    y^*; we call this distribution the "posterior"
    distribution, as opposed to the "prior," because it
    is posterior to observing the result of the experi-
    ment. Since the location operator was used in this
    experiment (to produce a location), we use the
    corresponding conditional distribution, $g_L(y|\theta)$.
    According to Bayes Theorem, we have

    $$f''_D(\theta|y^*) = \frac{f'_D(\theta)\ g_L(y^*|\theta)}{\int f'_D(\theta)\ g_L(y^*|\theta)\ d\theta}$$

2. The actions for which such a change in information
    takes place are only those which include the newly-
    generated action. In our example, these are location
    band D, band of interest B, and the set of all loca-
    tions, 0. (We assume that any information about the
    other band of interest, A, or the location band C,
    carried by the cost y^* is negligible compared to the

information gained about B, D, and O.) The change in information for these actions (B, D, O), will be computed according to Bayes Theorem as shown in (1). We will use the same likelihood function $g_L(Y|\theta)$ for each such computation, but the prior $f_j^!(\theta)$ will be that one specific to the action for which the change is being computed.

3. The engineer is only able to differentiate among actions which he has generated, in this sense: given some action A_j which has already been generated, the engineer has the same prior distribution $f_j(\theta)$ over all actions (of lower level) included in A_j, which have not yet been identified specifically by being generated in a search process. In our example, all location bands included in band of interest A have not yet been generated; therefore, the engineer is unable to differentiate among them, and so has the same prior distribution over each as over A itself. Similarly, any location bands in B other than the two already generated, C and D, have the same prior distribution as B; and, any other bands of interest, or location bands, which might be generated outside of either A or B have the same prior, represented as the prior over action O.

b) Detailed statement

1. There is a set of SLO's available for the engineer to use in solving a particular location problem. Each SLO defines a metric over the action space, and thus a set of actions. Identify uniquely each one of the non-elemental actions defined by these metrics with a value of the index k. (We disregard the elemental actions, produced by the elemental operator.) Let A denote the set of all non-elemental actions a_k, $k = 1, 2, \ldots, n$.

2. At a particular point in the location process, we have a list of all those actions which have been generated and evaluated. Let m denote the number of these actions which are non-elemental. (m = 0, 1, ..., n.) Without loss of generality, we can arrange the indexing of the actions a_k such that a_1, a_2, ..., a_m correspond to the m generated non-elemental actions, while a_{m+1}, ..., a_n correspond to those non-elemental actions which have not yet been generated. Thus, we can visualize the location process as a sequence of operations, where each operation consists of identifying some action in the ungenerated set, placing a cost on it, and moving it into the set of generated actions.

3. For any non-elemental action, a_k, there is a corresponding parameter θ_k, defined thus:

    Assume that the elemental operator is applied to a_k some number of times, n. The frequency distribution of costs of the resulting elemental actions is denoted as $h_k(c)$, c denoting cost. Let θ_k be any desired parameter of this distribution (e.g., the least cost of the n locations).

4. Let us define the vector $\theta = (\theta_1, \theta_2, ..., \theta_n)$ as the set of θ_k's for the full set of n non-elemental actions, A. Let us also define the vector $\pi_m = (\theta_1, ..., \theta_m)$ as the set of θ's for only those m non-elemental actions which have been generated at a particular point in the location process.

5. Let $F(\pi_m) = F(\theta_1, ..., \theta_m)$ denote the joint probability distribution over the θ_k's for those m non-elemental actions which have been generated. From this joint distribution, m marginal distributions $f_k(\theta)$ can be obtained. The function $f_k(\theta)$ is the probability that the parameter θ_k for action a_k takes the value θ.

The distributions F and f are subjective distributions; they represent the engineer's judgement about the relative likelihoods of different values of the parameters θ_k for the m generated non-elemental actions. Although we spoke explicitly only of the marginals $f_j(\theta)$ in Section 3, we are going to interpret these marginals in terms of the underlying joint distribution F.

6. Let $Q(\underline{\theta}) = Q(\theta_1, \ldots, \theta_n)$ denote the joint probability distribution over the θ_k's for all the non-elemental actions, whether or not generated. Let $q_k(\theta)$ denote the marginal distribution computed from $Q(\underline{\theta})$. Our objective now is to show the relationship between $Q(\underline{\theta})$ and $F(\underline{\pi}_m)$ by way of the respective marginals.

7. Least Including Action:

   Consider any ungenerated action a_k, $k = m+1, \ldots, n$. We define the Least Including Action for a_k as that one of the generated non-elemental actions a_j ($j = 1, 2, \ldots, m$) which

   i)   includes a_k, and

   ii) is the lowest-level generated action a_j which does so.

   We will symbolize the Least Including Action for a_k as a_k^*, where k^* is less than or equal to m.

8. Homogeneity assumption:

   For each ungenerated action a_k, $f_k(\theta) = f_{k^*}(\theta)$. That is, the engineer places the same probability distribution over the value of θ for an ungenerated non-elemental action a_k as he places over the lowest-level generated action which includes a_k.

68

We see that this assumption relates the distributions $Q(\theta_1, \ldots, \theta_n)$ and $F(\underline{\pi}_m) = F(\theta_1, \ldots, \theta_m)$ through their marginals. For $k = 1, \ldots, m$, $q_k(\theta) = f_k(\theta)$; for k greater than m, $q_k(\theta) = f_k^*(\theta)$, where k^* is the least including action for k.

9. This assumption says that before the engineer has generated and evaluated an action, he has no basis for distinguishing any difference between that action and any other ungenerated action which has the same least including action.[1] Furthermore, his prior over that action is the same as over the least including action. For example, before the engineer generates and evaluates a location, he has no reason for placing different prior distributions over two ungenerated location bands which have the same band of interest as their least including action; or for placing a different distribution over an ungenerated location band than over its least including band of interest.[2]

10. When the engineer generates an action a_k, moving it from the set of ungenerated non-elemental actions to the set of generated actions, he also obtains the value of some index y_k for that action (its cost, or some parameter of the distribution of costs - cf. Section 2.4).

---

[1] This does not imply that each such ungenerated action has the same probability of being generated by the engineer.

[2] There will be occasions at which the engineer does desire to differentiate between sets of locations. If he does make such a distinction, then he has essentially applied a Single-Level Operator, thereby generating and evaluating one or more actions; that SLO should be explicitly identified and incorporated into the analysis of the process, even if its operation is completely informal and instantaneous, and its cost trivial. The reason is that it is necessary to establish a level for these actions, in order to control the kind of actions which can be produced from them.

We assume that the engineer has enough information about his search and selection processes to characterize each of his SLO's with a function $g_i(y|\theta)$, where i specifies the operator. For a given action a_k for which the value of θ is θ_k, $g_i(y_k|\theta_k)$ gives the probability that the selection operation will assign a value y_k to this action.

11. Taking into account the uncertainty about θ_k, as expressed by $f_k(\theta)$, we can compute the unconditional probability of a value y for action a_k as:

$$P_{ijk}(y) = \int g_i(y|\theta)\, f_k(\theta)\, d\theta$$

12. We wish to obtain $P_{ij}(y)$, the probability that the result of the experiment e_{ij} will be an action with cost y. By the homogeneity assumption, we have $f_j(\theta) = f_k(\theta)$ for any action a_k which will be produced by this experiment (since every such action is included in a_j, and has a_j as its least including action). Let R denote the set of all ungenerated actions a_k which might be produced by e_{ij}: those actions which are included in j, and which are at the level such that they would be produced by operator i. Let p(k) be the probability that the action actually produced by e_{ij} is a_k, for k belonging to R. Then,

$$P_{ij}(y) = \sum_{k \in R} P_{ijk}(y)\, p(k)$$

$$= \sum_{k \in R} p(k) \cdot \int g_i(y|\theta)\, f_k(\theta)\, d\theta$$

By the homogeneity assumption, we have $f_j(\theta) = f_k(\theta)$ for k belonging to R, so

$$P_{ij}(y) = \int g_i(y|\theta)\, f_j(\theta) \sum_{k \in R} p(k)\, d\theta$$

70

$$P_{ij}(y) = \int g_i(y|\theta) \, f_j(\theta) \, d\theta$$

We see that this assumption allows us to ignore the question of which action is produced by the operator, so that we do not need to know $p(k)$. We work directly with the cost of the action produced.

13.   When the experiment e_{ij} is actually performed, the result is an action a_k^* and its cost, y^*. When the engineer observes the result y^*, his distribution over θ_k^* will, in general, change. We assume that this change can be computed by Bayes Theorem, using the likelihood function for the operator i which was used to generate a_k^*. Since $f'_j(\theta) = f'_k{}^*(\theta)$, we have

$$f''_j(\theta|y^*) = \frac{f'_j(\theta) \, g_i(y^*|\theta)}{P_{ij}(y^*)} \, ,$$

where $P_{ij}(y^*)$ is computed as in (12) above. As a consequence of the identity of the prior over a_k^* and the prior over a_j, the parent action, the posteriors f'' over both actions are identical.

14.   The result y^* of the experiment e_{ij} will not provide information about all actions a_k. That is, the priors $f_k(\theta)$ will not all be changed. We assume that information flows "vertically" only: only the priors of actions including the new one are revised. Thus, the revisions of the priors are assumed to follow these rules:

for all $k \supset k^*$: $f''_k(\theta|y^*) = \dfrac{f'_k(\theta) \, g_i(y^*|\theta)}{\displaystyle\int f'_k(\theta) \, g_i(y^*|\theta) \, d\theta}$

for $k = k^*$: $\qquad\qquad f''_k{}^*(\theta|y^*) = f''_j(\theta|y)$

for all other k: $\qquad f''_k(\theta|y^*) = f'_k(\theta)$

15. When the experiment performed involves the generation of an elemental action, the procedure for computing the changes in the prior in outline is the same. One difference is that an elemental action does not have a prior $f(\theta)$, and so does not have a posterior. The second difference is in the definition of the conditional distribution $g_i(y|\theta)$. For a non-elemental operator, we defined the two arguments y and θ as characteristics of the action produced, a_k. For the elemental operator, we deal directly with the θ for the parent action, θ_j, instead of indirectly via the homogeneity assumption.

16. In the course of the location process, a sequence of experiments are executed. Let:

$f'_j{}^{(n)}(\theta) = $ the prior before execution of the nth experiment;

$f''_j{}^{(n)}(\theta) = $ the posterior, after execution of the nth experiment;

$H_n = $ the results of the first n experiments, $(y_1^*, \ldots, y_n^*)$.

Then, $f'_j{}^{(n+1)}(\theta) = f''_j{}^{(n)}(\theta|H_n)$. This statement is not an assumption, but emphasizes that implicit in the notion of a "prior" $f'(\theta)$ is that it is conditional on all relevant past history, whether or not that past history is stated specifically.

For example:

$$f''_j{}^{(1)}(\theta | y_1{}^*) = \frac{f'_j{}^{(1)}(\theta)\, g_{i1}(y_1{}^* | \theta)}{\int f'_j{}^{(1)}(\theta)\, g_{i1}(y_1{}^* | \theta)\, d\theta}$$

$$f'_j{}^{(2)}(\theta) = f''_j{}^{(1)}(\theta | y_1{}^*)$$

$$f''_j{}^{(2)}(\theta | y_1{}^*, y_2{}^*) = \frac{f'_j{}^{(1)}(\theta)\, g_{i2}(y_2{}^* | \theta)}{\int f'_j{}^{(2)}(\theta)\, g_{i2}(y_2{}^* | \theta)\, d\theta}$$

$$= \frac{f''_j{}^{(1)}(\theta | y_1{}^*)\, g_{i2}(y_2{}^* | \theta)}{\int f''_j{}^{(1)}(\theta | y_1{}^*)\, g_{i2}(y_2{}^* | \theta)\, d\theta}$$

$$f''_j{}^{(2)}(\theta | H_2) = \frac{f'_j{}^{(1)}(\theta)\, g_{i1}(y_1{}^* | \theta)\, g_{i2}(y_2{}^* | \theta)}{\int f'_j{}^{(1)}(\theta)\, g_{i1}(y_1{}^* | \theta)\, g_{i2}(y_2{}^* | \theta)\, d\theta}$$

Note that the characteristic of the operator, $g_i(y | \theta)$ is assumed independent of past history; the effects of past experience upon the distribution of outcome of the experiment, $f(y)$, are represented by the $f(\theta | H)$ only.

17. These rules for revising the probability distributions
are expressed in terms of the marginals f_k of the
distribution $F(\underline{\pi}_m)$ over the m generated non-elemental
actions. These are the distributions with which the
engineer deals explicitly, in our model. We have noted
that as a result of the homogeneity assumption, this
"manifest" distribution F can be interpreted as representing a "latent" distribution Q, where Q is defined
over all non-elemental actions, whether or not generated.
(8, above.) In terms of this latent distribution, we
can give the following image of the evolution of a location process:

> When the process begins, the marginal distributions
> $f(\theta_k)$ over the components θ_k are identical, because
> no actions have been generated. Each time an
> experiment is executed, one or more marginals become
> differentiated. As the process unfolds through the
> execution of experiments, more and more marginals
> go off on separate paths, in a complex and inter-
> related manner determined by the inclusion relation-
> ships among the actions.

A series of prototype computations is presented in outline in
Figure II-6.

FIGURE II-6   CALCULATIONS ILLUSTRATING FLOWS OF
             INFORMATION OVER A SERIES OF
             EXPERIMENTS.

A. Two operators, $i = 1,2$ (2 = elemental operator)

B. Stage I.

    i) Status:

        one "action", the domain of all possible actions

no.	label	level	distribution
1	00	3	$f_{00}^1(\theta)$

(00)

    ii) Experiment;

        operator 2 on action 1:   (2;00)

        produces action (01) with cost y_{01}^*

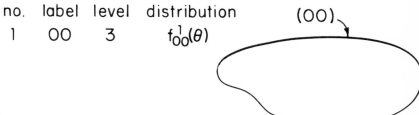

$$f_{00}^{11}(\theta/y_{01}^*) = \frac{f_{00}^1(\theta)\, g_2(y_{01}^*/\theta)}{\int f_{00}^1(\theta)\, g_2(y_{01}^*/\theta)\, d\theta}$$

(00)

(01)

$H_1 = (y_{01}^*)$

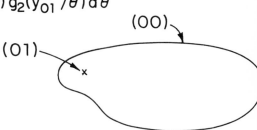

C. Stage II:

    i) Status:

no.	label	level	distribution	cost (elemental actions only)
1	00	2	$f_{00}^{11}(\theta/y_{01}^*)$	——
2	01	1	——	y_{01}^*

    ii) Experiment:

        operator 1 on action 1   (1;00)

        produces action (10), with cost estimate y_{10}^*

(cont.)

FIGURE II-6 (continued)

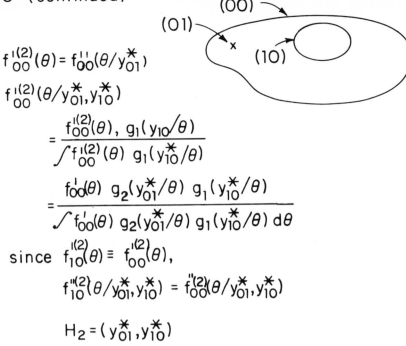

$$f_{00}^{I(2)}(\theta) = f_{00}^{II}(\theta / y_{01}^*)$$

$$f_{00}^{I(2)}(\theta / y_{01}^*, y_{10}^*)$$

$$= \frac{f_{00}^{I(2)}(\theta), \; g_1(y_{10}/\theta)}{\int f_{00}^{I(2)}(\theta) \; g_1(y_{10}^*/\theta)}$$

$$= \frac{f_{00}^{I}(\theta) \; g_2(y_{01}^*/\theta) \; g_1(y_{10}^*/\theta)}{\int f_{00}^{I}(\theta) \; g_2(y_{01}^*/\theta) \; g_1(y_{10}^*/\theta) \, d\theta}$$

since $f_{10}^{I(2)}(\theta) \equiv f_{00}^{I(2)}(\theta)$,

$$f_{10}^{III(2)}(\theta / y_{01}^*, y_{10}^*) = f_{00}^{III(2)}(\theta / y_{01}^*, y_{10}^*)$$

$$H_2 = (y_{01}^*, y_{10}^*)$$

D. Stage III.

i) Status:

no.	label	level	distribution	cost
1	00	3	$f_{00}^{III(2)}(\theta / H_2)$	——
2	01	1	——	y_{01}^*
3	10	2	$f_{00}^{III(2)}(\theta / H_2)$	——

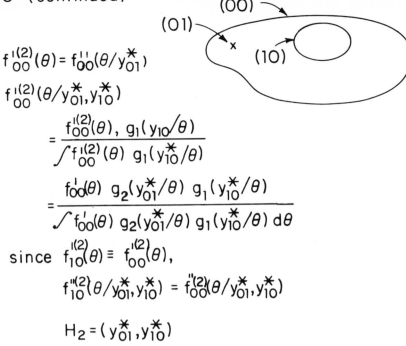

ii) Experiment:

operator 1 on action 1 (1;00)

produces action (20), with

cost estimate y_{20}^*

(00) ⊃ (20)

(10) ⊅ (20)

$$H_3 = (H_2, y_{20}^*) = (y_{01}^*, y_{10}^*, y_{20}^*)$$

therefore: $f_{00}^{III(2)}(\theta / H_2, y_{20}^*) = \dfrac{f_{00}^{III(2)}(\theta / H_2) \; g_1(y_{20}^*/\theta)}{\int f_{00}^{III(2)}(\theta / H_2) g_1(y_{20}^*/\theta) d\theta}$

(cont.)

76

FIGURE II-6 (continued)

$$f_{20}^{''(3)}(\theta/H_2,y_{20}^*) = f_{00}^{''(3)}(\theta/H_2,y_{20}^*)$$

$$f_{10}^{''(3)}(\theta/H_3) = f_{10}^{'(3)}(\theta/H_2) = f_{10}^{''(2)}(\theta/H_2)$$

iii) Comment:

note that information about (10) is <u>not</u> affected by information about (20)

E. Stage IV.

i) Status:

no.	label	level	distribution	cost
1	00	3	$f_{00}^{''(3)}(\theta/H_3)$	——
2	01	1	——	y_{01}^*
3	10	2	$f_{00}^{''(2)}(\theta/H_2)$	——
4	20	2	$f_{00}^{''(3)}(\theta/H_3)$	——

ii) Experiment:

operator 2 on action 3

$$(2;10)$$

produces action (11), with cost y_{11}^*

$$(00) \supset (11)$$
$$(10) \supset (11)$$
$$(20) \not\supset (11)$$

$$H_4 = (H_3,y_{11}^*) = (y_{01}^*,y_{10}^*,y_{20}^*,y_{11}^*)$$

therefore: $\displaystyle f_{10}^{''(4)}(\theta/H_3,y_{11}^*) = \frac{f_{10}^{'(4)}(\theta/H_3)\, g_2(y_{11}^*/\theta)}{\int f_{10}^{'(4)}(\theta/H_3)\, g_2(y_{11}^*/\theta)\,d\theta}$

$$= \frac{f_{00}^{''(2)}(\theta/H_2)\, g_2(y_{11}^*/\theta)}{\int f_{00}^{''(2)}(\theta/H_2)\, g_2(y_{11}^*/\theta)\,d\theta}$$

$$f_{00}^{''(4)}(\theta/H_3,y_{11}^*) = \frac{f_{00}^{'(4)}(\theta/H_3)\, g_2(y_{11}^*/\theta)}{\int f_{00}^{'(4)}(\theta/H_3)\, g_2(y_{11}^*/\theta)\,d\theta}$$

(cont.)

FIGURE II - 6 (continued)

$$= \frac{f_{00}^{'(4)}(\theta/H_3)\, g_2(y_{11}^{*}/\theta)}{\int f_{00}^{'(4)}(\theta/H_3)\, g_2(y_{11}^{*}/\theta)\,d\theta}$$

$$f_{20}^{''(4)}(\theta/H_3, y_{11}) = f_{20}^{'(4)}(\theta/H_3) = f_{00}^{''(3)}(\theta/H_3)$$

iii) Comment:

all the non-elemental actions now have different distributions since different parts of past history (H_4) are relevent to current information about their characteristics.

Tracing back to a common state, we have:

$$f_{20}^{''(4)}(\theta/H_4) = \frac{f_{00}^{''(2)}(\theta/H_2)\, g_1(y_{20}^{*}/\theta)}{\int f^{''(2)}(\theta/H_2)\, g_1(y_{20}^{*}/\theta)\,d\theta}$$

$$f_{10}^{''(4)}(\theta/H_4) = \frac{f_{00}^{''(2)}(\theta/H_2)\, g_2(y_{11}^{*}/\theta)}{\int f_{00}^{''(2)}(\theta/H_2)\, g_2(y_{11}^{*}/\theta)\,d\theta}$$

$$f_{00}^{''(4)}(\theta/H_4) = \frac{f_{00}^{''(3)}(\theta/H_3)\, g_2(y_{11}^{*}/\theta)}{\int f_{00}^{''(3)}(\theta/H_3)\, g_2(y_{11}^{*}/\theta)\,d\theta}$$

$$= \frac{f_{00}^{''(2)}(\theta/H_2)\, g_2(y_{11}^{*}/\theta)\, g_1(y_{20}^{*}/\theta)}{\int f^{''(2)}(\theta/H_2)\, g_2(y_{11}^{*}/\theta)\, g_1(y_{20}^{*}/\theta)\,d\theta}$$

It is seen that the only distribution influenced by every element in H is $f_{00}(\theta)$

6. The optimal experiment to do next

6.1 Statement of the problem

We state the problem thus:

We are at some point in the process of solving a route location problem. The engineer has available to him a number of sets of procedures for generating and costing out actions. We call each set of procedures a Single-Level Operator, and characterize each one by its level, its cost, and its probability characteristic. The status of the location process is expressed by a list of the actions which have already been generated and costed, together with their characteristics (sequence number, level, label, and prior probability distribution); we are also interested in the cost of the least-costly of the elemental actions (fully-specified locations) which have been produced so far.

At this point, with these operators and actions, the engineer has a number of choices open to him: he can elect to execute next any one of several experiments, or he can decide to terminate the location process.

Our objective in this section is to show how the model which we have been developing in this chapter can be used to explore the options available to the engineer and to determine which is optimal. The sense of optimal which we shall use is that of expected net return, where the probability distributions used for the expected-value computations are subjective or derived from subjective data. We shall be using the framework of Bayesian decision theory (BDT), somewhat modified. (For a discussion of Bayesian decision theory, see Appendix A.)

6.2 The decision tree

The first element required for the BDT analysis is the decision tree. This is essentially a list of all possible choices open to the engineer, and all possible events which are not under his control, arranged to indicate their sequence in time. In the location process, the choices are among experiments and actions. The events beyond the engineer's control are the outcomes of the experiments.

actions, a:[1] The terminal actions available to the engineer at any point in the location process are the elemental actions which have been generated so far (if any). We include the null alternative, i.e., not constructing the highway at all. Since we have assumed that we know the cost of an elemental action with certainty, the choice of a terminal action is simple: that elemental action with the lowest cost.

experiments, e: To define completely an experiment, we need to specify (a) the SLO to be used and (b) the non-elemental action to which the operator will be applied. (We use the notation introduced in Section 5.2.)

Of course, not all combinations of actions and SLO's form possible experiments. In particular, the application of an SLO to an action which has been produced by an SLO of the same or lower level is not defined. That follows from our definitions of non-elemental actions, of inclusion, and of level: an SLO of higher level produces an action which is "larger" - includes more actions - than the action produced by a lower-level SLO. Therefore, a higher-level action cannot be produced from within a lower level one.

---

[1] The notation used is that of Appendix A.

FIGURE II-7 TYPICAL DECISION TREE

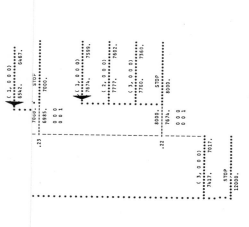

BEST EXPERIMENT TO DO NEXT IS OPERATOR 1 ,
ON ACTION 1 = 0 0 0 0

Examples of undefined experiments in a three-SLO process are:

(III, 101) - 101 is the product of SLO III

(II, 020) - 020 is the product of SLO II

(II, 021) - 021 is the product of SLO III, which is
of lower level than SLO II

(I, X Y Z) - is undefined for <u>any</u> x y z <u>except</u> (000).

As an example, let us look at a particular stage in a three-SLO process, and list the possible experiments which might be performed at the next stage:

a) List of actions:

Sequence No.	Label
1	000
2	100
3	110
4	001
5	010
6	200
7	201

b) Possible experiments for next stage:

(I, 000);

(II, 000), (II, 100), (II, 200);

(III, 000), (III, 100), (III, 200), (III 110), (III, 010).[1]

This list suggests the simple algorithm for determining whether a particular combination of (SLO, action) is defined and therefore a possible experiment: Let n be the number of SLO's available, and therefore the number of characters in the label identifying any action. Then, the application of SLO i to an action A is defined if and only if the right-most (n - i + 1) characters in A's identification label are all zeroes. (i = 1, ..., n.)

_____

[1] The actions resulting from each of these experiments have already been presented in Section 5.2.

<u>Results of an experiment, y:</u>[1] An experiment yields an action
and a cost associated with that action. For our purposes, the
action is characterized by its cost, and whether or not it is elemental. Therefore, we let the values of y denote the possible
costs of the action produced.

Although cost is continuous, we will always break costs up
into discrete ranges, as: $0-100, 101-200, etc.

<u>State of nature, θ; difference between our tree and the usual
BDT tree:</u> In the usual BDT application, the value of each terminal
action depends upon the unknown state of nature θ. However, in our
model, the value of a terminal action a is known with certainty,
and is its cost. We use θ in a different manner, letting it represent the future stream of experimental results: recall that in
Section 3.3 we gave θ an interpretation which is a function of the
set of costs of elemental actions generated in future experiments.

Because of this difference in significance of θ, the decision
tree we use has a simpler form than the one usual in BDT. As shown
in Figure 11-7, the decision tree is based upon the module of
(experiment, result), instead of the usual form (experiment, result,
action, state). (Compare with Figure A-1, in Appendix A.)

In this computer-produced tree, there are three vertical
columns. In the first column, on the left, there are three possible
experiments shown for the first stage: (1; 0 0 0), (2; 0 0 0), and
(3; 0 0 0), as well as termination. For each experiment, several
possible results are shown in the second column - for example, 6000.,
7000., etc. The decimal fraction immediately to the left of any

_____

[1] In Appendix A, z was used instead of y.

82

result branch is the probability of observing that result of the indicated experiment. In the third column, possible experiments at the second stage are shown, conditional upon the first stage experiment's having been performed and the first stage result's having been observed. The numbers immediately below the experiment and result branches are expected utilities; these will be explained in Section 6.5. The block of digits which begins below each result branch, for example "0 0 0" and "1 0 0", is the list of the actions which have been generated to that point in the location process. In the example shown, there are three operators available, and so each label has three characters.

6.3 Utility

We measure utility, or desirability, in dollars.

There are two major elements to utility in this context:
1.   the cost of executing an experiment;
2.   the cost of the best elemental action available
     as a solution to the location problem.
Although we have couched our discussion in terms of maximizing utility, we see that both elements of utility are costs. There-fore, we could also phrase our discussion in terms of costs, where the objective is to find the experiment with the minimum expected total cost.

In evaluating a particular experiment, we assume that the cost of executing the experiment is known with certainty; it is given as a function of the operator used in the experiment. The cost of the best elemental action so far generated is known also, with certainty. The only difficulty arises when we try to evaluate the return which an experiment brings us.

The return from an experiment is clearly a function of the result of the experiment. When the result is an elemental action better than the best found previously, we have got a tangible direct return. However, when the result is not an elemental action, or is an elemental action which is not an improvement, then the return is indirect, but present nevertheless. There are two forms which this indirect return can take. First, if the action produced was non-elemental, then there is additional freedom of choice for future applications of the elemental operator: we have one more non-elemental action from which to choose. Second, whether the new action is elemental or non-elemental, we learn something about the actions in which it is included. This information is reflected in the changes in the probability distributions $f_j(\theta)$ for those actions.

The formulation of a utility function must take into account both direct and indirect returns. The actual determination of such a utility function is intimately interwoven with the logic of the computations, and so we will defer detailed discussion until the next chapter. For the remainder of this chapter, we will assume that a procedure has been established for determining the utility of an experiment, which considers the cost of the experiment and both direct and indirect returns of the action which resulted.

6.4 Probability structure

There are two aspects of the probability structure important to us:

1. the probability distribution over the results of a proposed experiment, prior to its execution;
2. the change in this probability after the result of the experiment is known.

The basic definitions and calculations have already been illustrated: the first is given in Section 3.2, and the second is obtained in the same manner as the first, once the prior over the action has been revised in accordance with the rules summarized in Section 5.3.

6.5 Basic expected-value calculations

Single-stage decision tree:

Given the status of the location process, the calculation of the best experiment to do next follows this outline:
1. Examine a possible experiment, e_{ij}.
2. Examine a possible result of that experiment, y (y is the cost of the action produced by e_{ij}).
3. Compute $P_{ij}(y)$, the probability of that result y.
4. Given that result y, update the status of the process (Section 5 of this chapter):
   a) determine if the result reduces the cost of the best elemental action found so far;
   b) add the new action to the list of actions;
   c) compute the changes in the probability distributions over the previously-generated actions.
5. Determine $u(e_{ij}, y)$, the utility of having performed experiment e_{ij} and observed result y.
6. If all possible results y have not been examined, go back to (2) and examine another one.
7. When all possible results y have been examined, compute the expected utility $u^{*}(e_{ij})$:

$$u^{*}(e_{ij}) = \int P_{ij}(y) \cdot u(e_{ij}, y) \, dy.$$

8. If all experiments e_{ij} which are possible at this point in the process have not been examined, go back to (1) and pick another experiment.

9. The expected utility for immediate termination is the value of the best elemental action found so far.

10. Pick that experiment (including termination) which has the maximum expected utility, $u^*(e)$.

The logical flow of this computation is illustrated in Figure 11-8.

Multi-stage decision tree: The general sequence of the computation is the same, with this exception: the utility of an (experiment, result) combination at any stage is set equal to the expected utility of the best experiment at the following stage, where that expected utility computation takes into account the assumed experiments and results at preceding stages.   We illustrate the logic of this computation for a two-stage tree in Figure 11-9.

Notice that the computation for this two-stage tree proceeds by "tracing out" and "folding back" the tree.   That is, we go down a series of branches: first stage experiment, first stage result, second stage experiment, second stage result - until we decide to stop;   then we place a utility on that hypothesized history, and back up to explore other second-stage results;   when we exhaust the results, we compute the expected utility.   Then we back up one more stage, to explore another second-stage experiment, then move forward again to second-stage results.   In logical progression, we go in and out branches of the tree, exploring its every sequence. This "tree-tracing" nature of the computational logic is basic to the computer program we have developed, which we shall describe in detail in the next chapter.

FIGURE II-8 EXPECTED UTILITY COMPUTATION – SINGLE STAGE

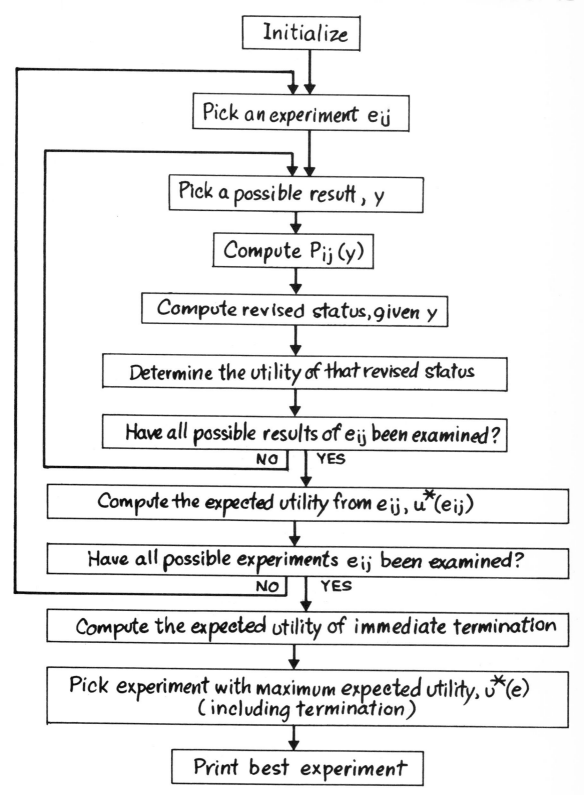

Initialize

Pick an experiment e_{ij}

Pick a possible result, y

Compute $P_{ij}(y)$

Compute revised status, given y

Determine the utility of that revised status

Have all possible results of e_{ij} been examined? NO YES

Compute the expected utility from e_{ij}, $u^*(e_{ij})$

Have all possible experiments e_{ij} been examined? NO YES

Compute the expected utility of immediate termination

Pick experiment with maximum expected utility, $u^*(e)$ (including termination)

Print best experiment

FIGURE II-9 EXPECTED UTILITY COMPUTATION - TWO STAGES

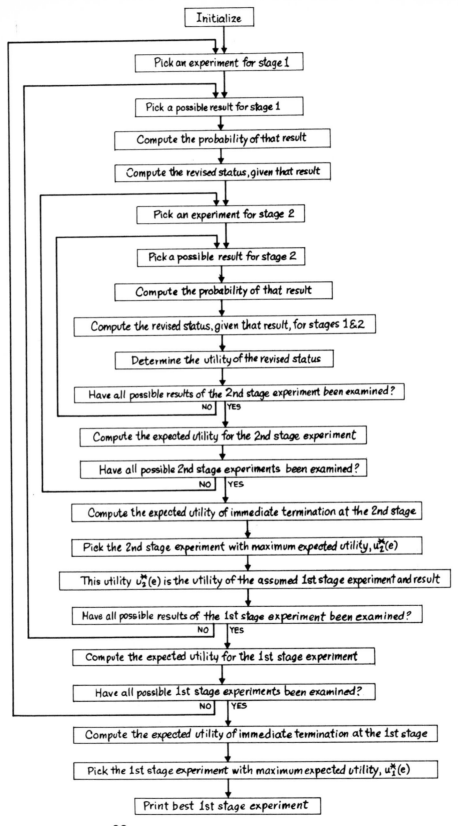

Relationship to the decision-tree diagram

The general structure of the decision-tree plot (Figure II-7) was described in Section 6.2 above. The only points not explained fully there concerned the expected utilities.

Under every branch corresponding to an experiment in this tree figure, there are two numbers. The left-most of the two is the total expected cost of the experiment; the right-most is the expected return from the experiment (considered as a cost). This return is equal to the total expected cost of the experiment less the cost of executing the experiment (i.e., the cost of the operator).

Under each result branch is the expected cost of the best experiment to do at the next stage, given that that result is observed. The return under the experiment branch at one stage is equal to the expected value of the expected costs for the next stage under the following result branches; the probabilities used to compute this expectation are those given immediately to the left of the result branches. (The result branches and their probabilities are shown only for the first stage, in this example.)

CHAPTER III

IMPLEMENTATION AND APPLICATIONS

The purpose of this chapter is to describe how the model has been implemented, in the form of a computer program, and to give some examples of the kinds of analyses for which it may be used.

We begin by describing the practical problems of implementing the computations required for the model, and then describe the approximations we have made in the computer program GUIDE I. To illustrate the use of the model, we show and discuss in detail the history of a hypothetical location process. We then illustrate several other kinds of analyses which can be done with this model. The chapter concludes with a brief discussion of the limitations of the present implementation.

1. Implementation of the model: GUIDE I

We finished the presentation of our model in the previous chapter with an outline of the computational procedure for computing the best experiment to do next. In outline, this procedure follows the logic of a Bayesian decision theory computation. However, the details are unique to our model - for example, the rules for updating the status of the process, and for constructing the decision tree (Chapter II).

The major problem in implementing this computational scheme is that of size: because the number of actions increases from stage to stage in the tree, the number of possible experiments goes up more than linearly with the number of stages, and so the number of possible combinations of experiments and results increases very rapidly as stages are added to the tree. On the other hand, the objective of the Bayesian decision theory approach is to consider all possible sequences, exploring their implications into the future as far as possible. Therefore, the desire to build and compute upon a tree with as many stages as possible is opposed by the practical realities of computing costs.

The first step in resolving this problem is to use a computer program to execute the computations. We have written a program for this purpose, called GUIDE I.[1] The flow charts for this program are given in Appendix II;[2] here, we will discuss only those limitations of the program which might affect its utility for implementing our model.

Although computerizing the computations makes the human cost (other than program development) significantly smaller, still the computations do take time. Therefore, approximations must be made.

The general nature of the computational approximations revolves around "cutting the tree" - that is, deciding when enough is known about the utility of a particular sequence of experiments and results so that it is not necessary to look further into the future. In many problems, if we traced the decision tree out far enough, we might be able to find its limits: that is, points where the optimal decision is clearly to terminate. It is not certain that we can do this, however, in all problems, and, as a practical matter, it is difficult to find these limits. Therefore, we must construct an approximate tree in which we balance the desire for completeness and accuracy against increases in computational costs.

---

[1] The "I" indicates our optimism about future, improved versions.

[2] A detailed write-up will be available shortly in the form of a program manual, GUIDE I: A COMPUTER PROGRAM FOR BAYESIAN DECISION THEORY COMPUTATIONS IN A HIERARCHICALLY-STRUCTURED SEQUENTIAL DECISION PROBLEM.

There are two interrelated aspects to the derivation of a reduced computationally-feasible tree.[1] First, there is the question of deciding where to terminate the analysis down any particular branch, because this results in the removal of whole subtrees of the original tree from consideration. The rules which are applied here are called "pruning" rules. Secondly, it is necessary to determine some equivalent value to be placed upon the termination point, to represent the value of the expected return of the optimal strategy in that part of the decision tree removed. These two questions are clearly related: for instance, the accuracy with which the expected return for a subtree can be approximated will influence the decision whether that subtree should be pruned away or computed down a few more levels.

We have both functions, pruning rules and terminal evaluation, in the computer program GUIDE I. In Figure III-1, we show the basic logic of this program. This is a generalization of the logic for the one- and two-stage computations shown in Chapter II (Figures II-8, II-9). There are several important additions, however; these are the decision blocks which control the computation by implementing the pruning rules, and the block in which terminal points in the tree are evaluated. We will explain these blocks in the following sections.

_____

[1] Minsky, Marvin, "Steps toward artificial intelligence," in Edward A. Feigenbaum and Julian Feldman, COMPUTERS AND THOUGHT. New York, McGraw-Hill (1963). p.431. Figure 10.

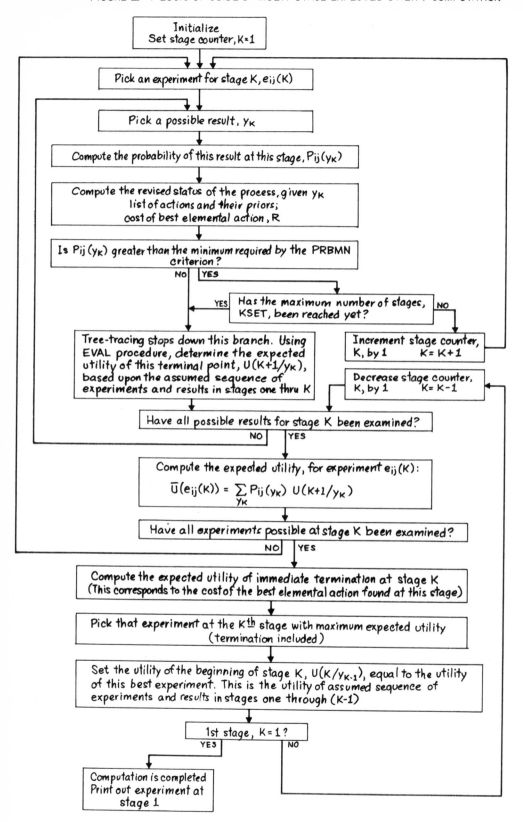

2. Pruning rules

There are many different rules which might be used to "prune" the tree. In the present version of GUIDE I, we use the following:

1. KSET: We set a maximum to the number of stages (combinations of experiments and results) for which the tree will be traced.[1] KSET is the parameter specifying this maximum number.

2. PRBMN criterion: For a particular result y at stage k (i.e., the cost of the action produced), compute the total probability of that result, which is the product of the probabilities of that result and of all results assumed for preceding stages. That is, if the history of results to that stage is $H_k = (y_1, y_2, \ldots, y_k)$, and if the probability of a particular result y_i at stage i, conditional on the past history H_{i-1}, is $P(y_i | H_{i-1})$,[2] then the total probability of the result y_k at stage k is

$$T = P(y_1)\, P(y_2|y_1)\, P(y_3|y_2,y_1)\, \cdots\, P(y_i|H_{i-1})\, \cdots\, P(y_k|H_{k-1})$$

$$= P(y_1) \prod_{i=2}^{k} P(y_i|H_{i-1}).$$

---

[1] This definition of the KSET rule will be modified in Section 3.3 below.

[2] Of course, each of these probabilities is based upon the experiments assumed at each of the preceding and present stages. To emphasize this, we could subscript each probability P with (i_k, j_k), but the typography would be too confusing.

The criterion value of probability for stage k is computed
in the same way, except that we replace the computed
conditional probabilities $P(y_i | H_i)$ by the values of the
parameters PRBMN(1), PRBMN(2), ..., PRBMN(k). If the
total probability T is less than the criterion value
given by PRBMN, then tracing of the tree ceases at that
stage, for that result.[1]

3. ANDREA criterion: For the possible experiments at any
    stage, consider only one experiment for each operator.
    We determine the best action upon which to apply a given
    operator in this way: if R is the cost of the best ele-
    mental action found so far, and $F_j(\theta)$ is the cumulative
    function for the prior $f_j(\theta)$, then the best action on
    which to use a given operator is that action, of those
    for which the experiment is defined, which has the max-
    imum $F(R)$.[2]

    Notice that we use the prior $f(\theta)$, and not the prob-
    ability distribution over the result of an application
    of the elemental operator, $P(y)$. We did this because

---

[1] The basic expected value computation proceeds by summing products
of the form $\Pi(y) = u(y)\ p(y)$, where y is a result, u(y) is the
utility of that result and p(y) its probability, conditional upon
past history. Professor Fleisher has pointed out that a better
criterion than PRBMN would be to examine the product $\pi(y)$ for
each y, and terminate at that result if this product were less
than some criterion value. The only difficulty with implementing
this more general criterion is that we need a preliminary evaluation of utility u(y) before we decide whether to proceed to a
more precise evaluation by continuing the tree-tracing. This is
an example of a general approach, the use of multiple evaluation
procedures, which should be explored in later experiments.
Cf. Section IV-2.10.

[2] ANDREA is the name of the subroutine where these computations
are performed.

98

using the latter would increase the time for this computation, and we felt that the number of situations in which the two distributions would give significantly different answers would be sufficiently small so that this increase in time would not be worthwhile.

This procedure needs to be supplemented with a tie-breaking rule, for the following two cases:

a) If no elemental action has yet been found, then R is generally such[1] that F(R) is unity for all actions. In this case, we compute a supplementary criterion,[2]

$$EPROB = \int_O^R (R-\theta)\ f(\theta)\ d\theta$$

$$= R \cdot F(R) - \int_O^R \theta\ f(\theta)\ d\theta$$

b) Since the last action generated and its immediate parent (least including action) have the same prior $f(\theta)$, they will have the same F(R) and EPROB values. The program favors the parent action in such a case.

---

[1] R may be set as input to any desired value, such as the value of the "null" solution, the existing condition. In our experiments we have set R to equal the maximum possible. Thus, in the examples shown here, each class interval equals $1000., and we allow up to 12 classes, so R = $12000.

[2] This criterion is based upon the formula derived in Section 3, q.v.

3. Evaluation procedure

The purpose of an evaluation procedure is to determine a utility to be assigned to a terminal position in the tree. Insofar as possible, the utility assigned should approximate the expected utility of the optimal sequence of experiments from that point on.

The procedure implemented in GUIDE I is somewhat complex. We shall develop our explanation of it in several steps.

3.1 Basic formulation: one experiment to go

We start by examining the following case: assume that the engineer will perform at most one more experiment beyond the given terminal point, and that that experiment will only be an elemental one.

Before the experiment contemplated is executed, the actions previously produced are known, as also their costs. If the proposed experiment were not executed, the best action for the engineer to take would be that elemental action with the lowest cost. Let R denote the cost of this action.

Assume that the elemental experiment will be executed once, and only once, and that after that experiment, the engineer will pick that action which has the lowest cost of all those elemental actions produced. The utility will be the value of that action. Letting y be the cost of the elemental action generated in the last experiment, the terminal action will have a cost equal to the lesser of R and y. Using c for the cost of the elemental operator, we have, for the cost of a given result,[1]

_____

[1] Note that u in this discussion is a cost.

(1)
$$u(e_{ij}, y) = c + \min(R, y).$$

We use $P_{ij}(y)$ for the indicated experiment to compute the expected cost:

(2)
$$u^{*}(e_{ij}) = \int_{o}^{\infty} P_{ij}(y) \, u(e_{ij}, y) \, dy$$

$$= c + \int_{o}^{R} y \, P_{ij}(y) \, dy + R \int_{R}^{\infty} P_{ij}(y) \, dy.$$

In comparison with this, we have the cost of immediate termination at the terminal position,

(3)
$$u^{*}(e_{o}) = R.$$

The engineer will choose the experiment e_{ij} over immediate termination only if

(4)
$$u^{*}(e_{ij}) < u^{*}(e_{o})$$

that is, if

$$\left[c + \int_{o}^{R} y \, P_{ij}(y) \, dy + R \int_{R}^{\infty} P_{ij}(y) \, dy \right] < R$$

or,[1]

(5)
$$\int_{o}^{R} (R-y) \, P_{ij}(y) \, dy > c.$$

---

[1] The integral on the left side of the inequality is what Raiffa and Schlaiffer call the "left-hand linear-loss integral." Raiffa, Howard, and Schlaifer, Robert, APPLIED STATISTICAL DECISION THEORY. Boston: Division of Research, Graduate School of Business Administration, Harvard University, p. 97, (1961).

That is, the engineer will choose experiment e, only if the expected reduction in the cost of the best elemental action found, is greater than the cost of the experiment.

Now, the elemental operator can be applied to any action j; therefore, the expected cost of the best elemental experiment, e, is

$$(6) \qquad u^*(e) = \min_j \ u^*(e_{ij}).$$

The expected cost of the best experiment, considering termination, is

$$(7) \qquad u^* = \min \left[u^*(e_o), \ u^*(e) \right] = \min \left[u^*(e_o), \ \min_j \ u^*(e_{ij}) \right].$$

We use the fact that

$$(8) \qquad u^*(e_{ij}) - R = c + \int_o^R y \ P_{ij}(y) \ dy + R \left[\int_R^\infty P_{ij}(y) \ dy - 1 \right]$$

$$= c - \int_o^R (R-y) \ P_{ij}(y) \ dy$$

to get:

$$(9) \qquad u^* = \min \left\{ R; \ R + \min_j \left[u^*(e_{ij}) - R \right] \right\}$$

$$= R + \min \left[0; \ c - \max_j \int_o^R (R-y) \ P_{ij}(y) \ dy \right].$$

3.2 Extension to four stages: EVAL

This equation (9) gives us the expected cost of the best experiment, under the assumption that we will perform at most one more experiment with the elemental operator. Now let us step back one stage and replace this with the assumption that we will produce at most two elemental actions. Let us denote this stage as (n-1), and then the last stage becomes stage n. Furthermore, let us assume that we will not change our probability distributions $P_{ij}(y)$ as a consequence of the first result; and that we will produce both elemental actions from the same parent action, that one which was found best by the ANDREA criterion at stage (n-1).

Therefore, equation (9) derived above gives the expected utility at stage n as a function of the cost of the best elemental action found to that stage, R_n, and the prior over the best action:

$$(10) \quad u_n^*(R_n) = R_n + \min\left[\; 0;\; c - \int_o^{R_n} (R_n - y_n)\; P_{ij}(y_n)\; dy_n \right]$$

where j is the best action according to ANDREA, i is the elemental operator, and y_n is the cost of the last elemental action generated.

Now considering the result of the previous stage, y_{n-1}, we see that $R_n = \min(R_{n-1}, y_{n-1})$. Therefore, we can also write the above as

$$(11) \qquad\qquad u_n^*(R_n) = u_n^*(R_{n-1}, y_{n-1}).$$

Then, looking at the situation from the beginning of stage (n-1), where we still have up to two elemental actions to be produced, we have, analogous to (7) above:

$$(12) \quad u_{n-1}^{*}(R_{n-1}) = \min \left[u_{n-1}^{*}(e_{o}); \quad u_{n-1}^{*}(e_{ij}) \right] = \min \left[R_{n-1}; \right.$$

$$\left. c + \int_{o}^{\infty} u_{n}^{*}(R_{n-1}, y_{n-1}) \, P_{ij}(y_{n-1}) \, dy_{n-1} \right].$$

Again, i is the elemental operator, and j is the same action as in (10).

This recursive formulation can be extended to any number of stages we desire. In our actual evaluation procedure in subroutine EVAL of GUIDE I, we have extended this relation to a total of four stages. That is, EVAL assumes that the engineer will generate at most four more elemental actions; that the probability distributions over the actions will remain unchanged by the results observed; that the same action will remain optimal according to the ANDREA criterion (this follows from assuming the priors do not change); and that the engineer will decide after each result whether to go on and generate an additional elemental action.

Note that in this formulation we do retain a sequential characteristic, in that the engineer need not generate all four elemental actions. Therefore, we cannot model this by obtaining the distribution of the least of four observations from the same distribution $f(\theta)$.

Note also that this is different from our general model, in
the important respect that the changes in the engineer's information as a result of the observed costs are not taken into account
in these four stages. Since we ignore this information change,
and limit the experiments at each stage to one, we can reach out
these four stages at a reasonable cost in computation time.

3.3 General evaluation procedure

The basic procedure in EVAL follows the above recursive
formulation over four stages. Evaluation of the terminal point
when the PRBMN (minimum total probability) criterion is not met
proceeds precisely in this way. However, when the reason for
stopping the tree-tracing along a branch is that the KSET criterion
(maximum number of stages) is exceeded, then we add an additional
phase to this evaluation procedure.

When KSET is exceeded, we do not stop the computation and
transfer to EVAL immediately. Rather, we allow one additional
stage of the computations, revising the priors and in general
doing everything as in the normal calculation. The only exception is that we allow but one experiment, at this additional stage
beyond KSET, and that is the best experiment in which the elemental operator is used. At the end of this one additional stage,
we then proceed to EVAL, for the analysis of up to four additional
elemental actions.[1]

_____

[1] This does not show up in the flow chart in Figure III-1, because
it is controlled in Subroutine PERMIS (cf. Flow chart, Appendix B).

The reasoning behind this distinction is thus: generally, when the PRBMN criterion is not met, the results have fairly small probabilities. When the KSET criterion is exceeded, however, there are a number of results at that last stage which have large probabilities. Therefore, more accuracy is necessary in the evaluation of the terminal points in the latter case, than in the former. We try to achieve greater accuracy by inserting the additional elemental experiment, and we try to get some representation of information gain, and of the flexibility of having alternative non-elemental actions to choose from, by running the full model (i.e., with status updating and ANDREA operation). We hope thereby to achieve improved accuracy at a relatively low additional cost in computing time.[1]

We were led to this last formulation in several steps. First, we tried to evaluate a terminal position simply by using the cost of the best elemental action. This meant that at the last stage there was wasted calculation in exploring any experiments except those with the elemental operator (since only that operator could produce a reduction in the utility). The next step was the formulation presented in Section 3.1, in which we assume that there will be at most one additional elemental action generated. After a number of trial computations, we began to feel that the operators of higher levels were being underrated: although we tried significant disparities in the costs of the different operators, we still found it difficult to get conditions under which experiments with the higher-level operators would become optimal. Therefore, we concluded that greater accuracy was needed in evaluating the terminal position, and so the present procedure was implemented.

---

[1]Of course, a great many variations on this combination could be used: variations in the numbers of stages with information change and without; variations in the use of ANDREA; etc. Further experiments should include extensive comparisons of computing times and differences in computed results, to get a better judgement as to the relative desirabilities of different combinations.

4. Applications of the model

Potential applications of this model can be divided into two classes: those oriented toward determining the best experiment to do next in a specific problem situation; and those which have as their objective the analysis of typical, or prototype, location problems.

4.1 Best experiment to do next

The basic computation for which the model (and the computer program GUIDE I) have been designed is that posed in the last section of Chapter I: given the state of the location process, to compute the optimal experiment for the engineer to perform next. This implies that every time the engineer executes an experiment, he returns to the computer, inputs the result of the executed experiment, computes his revised status, and then computes the optimal next experiment.

The most immediate extension of this computation follows from the logic of the actual computation itself. The computation proceeds by the construction of an extensive tree and the determination of the optimal experiment at every decision point in that tree. Therefore, in principle, it is necessary to perform these computations only once, constructing the full tree of all possible sequences of experiments (for given priors and operator costs and distributions). Then, after executing each experiment, the engineer would examine this tree and simply pick off by inspection that experiment which was optimal for the next step.

In practice, this is not feasible, because limitations of computing time in the present program indicate that the cost of

constructing the full tree for a problem will generally be prohib-
itive. Therefore, the engineer is required to return to the computer periodically for computation of the optimal experiment forward from his current state.[1]

In Section 5, we illustrate the best-experiment computation
in a hypothetical location problem. This example is carried
through a sequence of experiments, until the optimal choice is
to terminate.

4.2 Analyses of prototype problems

Besides the basic "next-experiment" type of computation, the
model can be used for a variety of interesting analyses. These
analyses focus on the expected costs of the experiments at the
next stage, particularly the best experiment, and explore the
changes in these costs as the nature of the problem is varied.

A location problem is defined by the list of actions and their
priors, and by the number, costs, and probability characteristics
of the operators. Given these data for a particular problem, we
can explore the way in which the expected costs of the experiments
change as a function of:

- a) changes in the costs of the operators, absolutely, or relative to one another;
- b) changes in the probability characteristics of the opera- tors, such as a shift in the mean, a change in variance, or skew;
- c) changes in one or more of the priors;

----

[1] This limitation in the existing program is particularly clearly
indicated by a mistake we made in constructing the example which
follows later in this chapter. Cf. Section 5.4, below.

d) the introduction of additional operators;

e) restrictions upon the engineer's freedom to choose any experiment he desires.

In Section 6, we illustrate the effects of varying operator characteristics. In Section 7, we identify a number of typical constraints on the engineer's choice of experiments, and illustrate the effects of these constraints with an example.

5. History of a location process: an example

5.1 Description of the example

To illustrate the behavior of our model, we have constructed a history of a hypothetical location process. This history is shown graphically in Chart A (in the pocket inside the back cover).

This chart is divided into three major sections, reading down the sheet, entitled: "Operator characteristics;" "Status of process;" and "Decision trees." The uppermost section shows the characteristics of the three operators: their costs, and their probability distributions.[1] The next two sections, status of process and decision trees, show the actual evolution of the location process, going from left to right, and are further divided into nine vertical columns.

In the left-most of these vertical columns, we show the initial state of the process. Reading down the chart in this column, we show in the status section the previous experiment performed and the probability distribution over the actions generated so far. In this first column, we have only the action (000), so there is one distribution. Passing down this column to the decision trees section, we have the tree for this initial position in the location process; at the bottom of the tree, we have the result of the computation, the best experiment to do next - (1; 000).[2]

---

[1] The probability distributions for the operators are given in the form $g(m)$, where $m = y-\theta$; cf. Section II-3.5.

[2] Because programming Roman numerals is somewhat messy, the computer plots shown in these figures have Arabic numerals to designate the SLO used in an experiment. For consistency with these plots in this discussion, we shall also use Arabic numerals.

The second vertical column indicates the point in the process where we have executed the experiment (1; 000) and determined that the cost of the action produced, (100), was $8000. The status part of the figure shows this new action added to the tree, and the new probability distributions. The decision tree indicates that, having performed this experiment and observed the result of $8000., the best experiment to do next is again (1; 000).

In this way, the sequence of nine vertical columns gives the history of the location process. Each column is obtained from the preceding one by executing the indicated experiment and observing a particular result. The process ceases with position H, where the computed optimum experiment turns out to be immediate termination.

The basic elements of the decision tree plots were explained in Sections 11-6.2 and 11-6.5; we will review them here. We examine the tree in the left-most vertical column, corresponding to position 0. Within this tree itself, there are three vertical columns: in the first column, we have four possible experiments for the first stage - (1; 000), (2; 000), (3; 000), and "STOP," (i.e., termination of the process). Following each experiment, we have in the second vertical column of this tree the possible results of that experiment: for example, following (1; 000) we have the results $5000., 6000., 7000., 8000., and 9000. (The results 1000-4000, and 10000-12000 have been eliminated by the operation of the PRBMN pruning rule. In this example, PRBMN = .10 for the first stage, .15, for the second, .25, for the third, and .30 for the fourth.) To the left of each result branch is the probability of that result - for example, for $5000. following (1; 000) the probability is 0.11. Underneath the result branch is the list of actions at that point - (000) and (100) in this case.

111

In the third vertical column of the tree, we show the experiments at the following stage: for example, if (1; 000) is the
first stage experiment, $8000. the first-stage result, then at
the second stage we show the experiments (1; 000), (2; 000), and
(3; 000). (Because of the operation of the KSET criterion -
KSET = 2 in these examples - we have only two stages in the tree.)
For each experiment, we show its total expected cost - for (1; 000)
and $8000. at the first stage, we have $7252. for (1; 000) at the
second stage, $7326. for (2; 000), etc. Then, with a small arrow
we indicate the best of these second-stage experiments - (1; 000)
in this case. The expected cost of this best experiment then
becomes the cost associated with the result, and shown under the
corresponding result branch.

Examining now the first-stage experiment (1; 000), the right-
most of the two numbers under that branch, $6980., is the expected
cost of performing the optimal experiment at the second stage. This
is calculated from the probabilities of the results and the costs
associated with those results. The left-most of these two numbers
is the total expected cost of the experiment ($7055. here), obtained
by adding the cost of the operator ($175. here) to the previous cost
($6980).

The large arrowheads, pointing to the right, indicate the
relationship between the decision trees for successive positions
in the process. For example, the large arrowhead just to the right

112

of the decision tree in the first column follows the experiment (1; 000) and result $8000. at the first stage, indicating that the next column shows the point in the process where (1; 000) has been executed and the result $8000. has been observed.

Note that in any particular column there is no probability distribution shown for an action which has not yet been generated. This does not imply that there is no distribution over those actions. Rather, on the basis of the homogeneity assumption introduced in Section II-5.3, each of these actions not yet generated has the same distribution as its least including action. Thus, for example, at position B, action (110) would have the same distribution as (100), (300) would have the same distribution as (000), etc.

This particular history was obtained by executing at each step that experiment which was found to be optimal.[1] (There is one exception: the application of operator 2 at position B is not optimal. This is discussed in Section 5.4 below.) The results, namely the costs of the actions produced, were selected so as to produce an interesting history. We wanted to show clearly how the priors would change, and how the optimal experiment would vary. We also wanted to get a set of actions with a sufficiently complex set of inclusion relationships so that the effects of the ANDREA criterion could be demonstrated.

We used three operators, because this indicates a number of interesting interactions, and allows an interesting competition among the operators. However, it is not so many as to make the computations excessively lengthy. We established the costs and the probability characteristics of these operators, after a

_____

[1] Optimal in the limited sense established by our computational approximations.

number of trials, such as to produce a situation in which no
single operator was clearly better than the other under all
conditions.[1]

All the probability distributions and results are discrete,
defined over 12 classes, with a class size of $1000. Therefore,
the possible results of any experiment which are considered
range thus: $1000., 2000., 3000., ..., 12000.

The prior over the single action at the first position,
(000), represents what we think a typical prior in a location
problem will be like: skewed to the left, to indicate that the
engineer is more certain of a lower bound on the cost, than of
an upper bound.

In the following discussion, it is important to keep clear
the distinction between "stage" and "position." A stage consists
of the choice of an experiment and the observation of a result.
A position is a point in the process, separated from another
position by a stage: for example, position A is one stage past
position 0, position B is two stages past, etc. When we speak
of the first stage in a tree, we mean the first experiment and
result following the indicated position. So, the second stage
following position 0 is the first stage following position A,
etc. Stages are measured relative to positions.

----

[1] More specifically: we did not want the costs so low that the
accuracy of the computations became critical. (We may not have
achieved this - cf. Section 5.4.) We did not want the costs
too high, because we desired for it to be possible to use operator 3 more than once (cf. discussion in Section 6), and we
wanted operators 1 and 2 to be useful under some conditions.
Finally, we wanted operator 2 to be somewhat worse than the
optimum, so that the constraints experiments (cf. Section 7)
would prove interesting.

Finally, let us emphasize that although we discuss their effects separately all the pruning rules - KSET, PRBMN, and ANDREA -are operating concurrently in the program, together with the evaluation procedure.

5.2   Effects of ANDREA and the evaluation procedure

The basic operation of the ANDREA criterion is clearly demonstrated in the tree for position A.   For example, examine the experiment (1; 000).   Before execution of this experiment (000) and (100) have the same distribution;   after this experiment, the new action (200) and its parent (000) will have the same distribution, but this will be different from the distribution over (100), which will be unchanged.   If the cost of (200) is $6000., $7000., or $8000., we see that the distribution over (200) and (000) will be more favorable than that over (100). (The sense of "favorable" is that defined by ANDREA, namely that $F(R)$ is greater for (000) than for (100).)   Therefore, the best use of operators 2 and 3, at the next stage, will be on action (000), as indicated in the tree.   On the other hand, if the results are $9000. or higher, (100) will be more desirable, as shown.

The relationship of the evaluation procedure to this ANDREA criterion is also illustrated here.   Note that even though the distribution over (100) is unchanged by the results of (1; 000), the expected cost of both second-stage experiments (2; 100) and (3; 100) depend upon the result ($9000. or $10000.).   This is because operator 3 at the next (third) stage will be applied to that action of (000), (100), (200), (110), which is best by the ANDREA criterion, and this will depend upon the result of the second-stage experiment, (2; 100) say, as it affects the prob-

ability distributions. For example, if the ANDREA criterion
required (2; 100) at the second stage, and the second stage
result came out unfavorable, the elemental operator at the
third stage would be applied to (000) if that was now best by
the ANDREA criterion.

In the tree for position F, we observe a more complicated
interaction, following experiment (2; 300). For both operators 2 and 3, the optimal action for an experiment at the
second stage shifts with the result. A first-stage result of
6000. or 7000. would recommend another try at (300) with operators 2 and 3. For a result of 8000. or 9000., a shift occurs.
(110) becomes desirable for operator 3. However, (2; 110) is
not a defined experiment (since (110) has been produced by
operator 2), and, therefore, that operator must take the next-
best action, (200).

Similar patterns are observable following (2; 100) at
position E, and elsewhere in the trees.

For (3; 110) at position F, the effect of ANDREA brings
about 3 changes: depending upon the first stage result, (000),
(200), or (300) is most desirable. Since (112) is included
only in (000) (of these three actions), we know that the
distributions $f(\theta)$ over (200) and (300) remain the same regardless of the result of (3; 110). What happens here is that R,
the value of the best elemental action, is changed for results
of 6000. and 7000. Although the cumulatives $F(\theta)$ remain the
same functions, we now use different points R' to obtain the
criterion F(R'). Thus, the effect of ANDREA through both the
distribution and R is demonstrated by these changes at position F.

At position D, following (2; 100) there is a shift at the second stage between (100) and (000). At present, this is unexplained.

Following (1; 000) at position E, we observe that there is almost no change at stage 2 in either the experiments to perform, or their returns. This arises from these three conditions: (a) the result (400) will not affect the distributions over (100) or (110); (b) the result will not affect the value of the best elemental action found so far; and (c) the result will not affect the sequence of the next five elemental operator applications. This suggests that a heuristic is necessary to avoid this redundant computation; but much more investigation is required before the necessary a priori criterion can be developed.

This same phenomenon occurs also at positions F and G. What seems to be happening is that a point has been reached at which the actions are numerous and relatively independent, so that one experiment does not have very far-reaching effects. This does not seem to be due simply to the computational approximations; we did a second run at G, with the number of stages increased by one, and found no significant change in the situation beyond (1; 000). This is suggested also by the results in our figure for this position, where we see that the expected costs of (2; 300) and (3; 300) for stage 1 are very close to those for the same experiments performed at stage 2, after (1; 000).

At position B, the optimal experiment at the second stage, following (1; 000), varies markedly. This fluctuation can be explained as the superposition of two effects. First, we have the effect of ANDREA, which judges (000) as optimal for results 8000. or less, and (100) optimal for results 9000. or 10000. Second, there is the competition between operators applied to the same action: operator 3 is better than operator 1, for action (000), for results 6000. and 7000. For action (100), the competition is between operators 2 and 3, since operator 1 cannot be applied to action (100).

Notice that at position H, there is no equivocation about whether termination is optimal. For, no matter what the first-stage experiment performed and the result observed are, the optimal experiment at the second stage is termination as well.

5.3 Effects of PRBMN

To investigate the effects of the probability cut-offs, we can compare Figure 11-7, and Position 0 of Chart A. The values of PRBMN used were:

STAGE	11-7	CHART A
1	.15	.10
2	.25	.15
3	.30	.25
4	.30	.30

An increase in PRBMN has the direct effect of reducing the number of result branches which are examined. The plots show the differences in the first stage results; not shown are the differences in the second stages.

The indirect effects are in the expected costs for each experiment. We see that the changes for the first-stage experiments are small, as this summary table of expected costs shows:

EXPERIMENT	II-7	CHART A	DIFFERENCE
(1; 000)	$7080.	$7055.	$25.
(2; 000)	7277.	7270.	7.
(3; 000)	7417.	7429.	-12.

The difference in expected cost of (1; 000) between the two levels of PRBMN is $25., one-third of the cost of that experiment. However, the differences between the costs of the best and second-best experiments are approximately $200. in both cases, so the $25. difference would not affect the decision at the first stage.

We find larger differences in the expected costs for the second-stage experiments. The extreme is (1; 000), after (1; 000) and a result of 6000., where the difference is about $90. However, most of the second-stage experiments after (1; 000) and (2; 000) have cost differences of $20.-40.

The experiments after (3; 000) have very much smaller differences, all less than $5. This suggests to us that the accuracy of the evaluations depends upon whether there has been at least one elemental action produced, with a cost within the range of the prior distributions. However, further experiments are necessary to evaluate this hypothesis.

As a result of comparisons like the one just described, we concluded that a good rule of thumb was to have a minimum probability of .10 in the first stage, .15 in the second, and .25 in the third. This seemed a good balance between computational time and accuracy.

Clearly, much more extensive experiments need to be done.

5.4 Accuracy

Let us first try to establish what we would mean by an "accurate" computation. I think Schlaifer's suggestion[1] is a good one: we should like to achieve a level of computation such that even if we increase the amount of computation which we do, the decision at the first stage does not change. Put this way, we emphasize the desire to spend as little for computation as possible, while at the same time indicating that our primary interest is a preference ordering over alternative experiments.

From the limited experiments we have done, a preliminary indication can be gained as to whether our computations are "accurate," in this sense. For example, from this history of a process, we can make the following comparison for each position in the process: compare the expected costs computed for each first-stage experiment at position N, with the expected costs computed at position (N-1), where those experiments were second-stage experiments. For example, the experiment (1; 000) as a first-stage experiment at position A has an expected cost of $7242. From position 0, considering the same experiment as a second-stage experiment following (1; 000) and a result of $8000., the expected cost is $7252., or $10. less. In this manner, we have constructed the following table:

---

[1] Schlaifer, Robert, PROBABILITY AND STATISTICS FOR BUSINESS DECISIONS: New York: McGraw-Hill, (1959), p. 601.

Differences in expected costs: (1st stage at position N+1) - (2nd stage at position N)

POSITION:	0	A	B	C	D	E	F	G
N =	1	2	3	4	5	6	7	8
OPERATOR:								
1	-10.	-1.	+5.	-4.	-1.	+7.	-23.	0.
2	+ 1.	+25.	+7.	-30.	-6.	-13.	+18.	0.
3	-30.	+8.	+29.	+2.	+3.	+8.	+11.	0.
Differences between best experiment and 2nd best at N:	197.	83.	21.	6.	85.	48.		72.	82.

Note that we have also shown the difference between the expected costs of the best and second-best experiments at each position.[1] This gives a rough idea of the significance of the differences tabulated between stages. It is only at positions B and C that the computations are sufficiently inaccurate as to suggest, by comparison with the difference between the best and second-best actions, that a different decision might possibly result from increased computation.

Notice that in position A, for a first-stage experiment (1; 000) and a result of 9000., the best second-stage experiment is (2; 100) with a cost of $7455. This is practically identical to (1; 000) which has a cost of $7456. Comparison with the computed values at position B indicates a reversal: (1; 000) turns out to be best at the first stage, with an expected cost of $7455., while (2; 100) is now evaluated at $7480. The effect of this at A is negligible, since the expected cost remains $7455 although the experiment has changed.

_____

[1] These numbers are not related directly to those above them in the table.

This switch did have this one effect, however, in our development of this example. Not anticipating this switch, we proceeded to develop the process from position B onward, assuming that (2; 100) was indeed optimal from B. This was done without checking carefully the computation from B. The result is that our example has optimal choices of experiment at every point in the process, except at B. However, we do not think the example has lost anything thereby.

We show in Figure III-2 the expected cost of the best experiment for each operator, as a function of position in the process, for each of three operators and termination. These costs were obtained from the first stages of the decision trees in Chart A. This figure clearly indicates that there is a general trend to the expected costs which is a function of the status of the process (the list of actions, their relationships, and their priors). The differences among the costs of these experiments are not very large, compared to the differences between the costs for one position and the next.

This emphasizes that small differences in expected costs of the experiments are important. This is a conclusion which we had not anticipated; and our approximation techniques are pretty crude relative to this discrimination requirement, where an error of one-half of one percent may be important. The ANDREA criterion, for example, may be too crude, in that the dominated actions, which are rejected as experiments, may <u>not</u> have expected costs which are so significantly different from the dominating one.

Further investigation in this area is required, and with some minor modifications in printout the existing program may be useful for this.

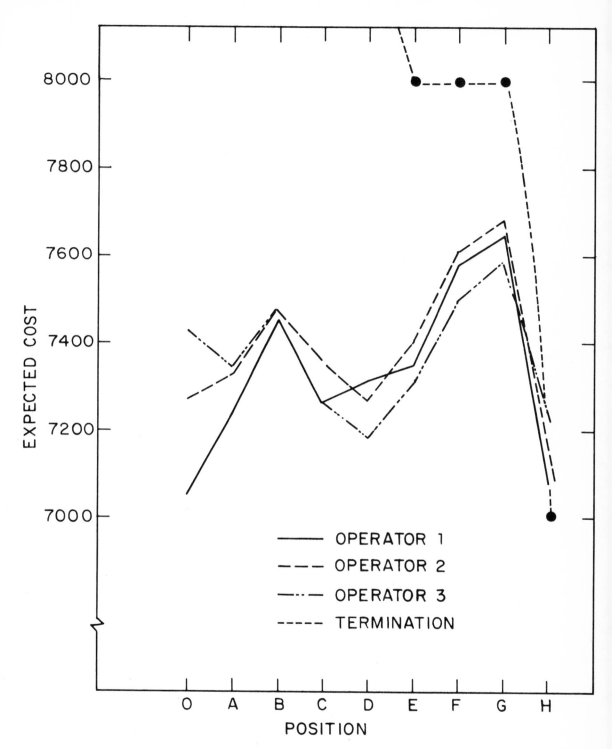

FIGURE III-2   EXPECTED COST AS FUNCTION OF POSITION IN
PROCESS

In retrospect, we have concluded that perhaps the most important approximation is our use of discrete probability distributions. For example, in this problem the probability distributions were defined with respect to twelve classes, each class
having a range of $1000. This is seen in the plots in the spac-
ing of the results, as: $5000., $6000., etc. Now, in a majority
of positions in the tree, the optimal experiment at the second
stage does not shift radically with the first-stage result. But
there are sufficiently many instances where this does happen,
that class size may indeed be a critical source of error in the
computations. This, too, requires further investigation.

6. Variation of operator characteristics: example

In Figure III-3, we show several experiments in the variation of operator characteristics. Parts (a) and (b) of this
figure illustrate the effects of varying the costs of operators.
Part (b) corresponds to position 0 of our location process
example (Chart A), and the three operators have the same characteristics as in that example. Part (a) corresponds to the
same position, except that the costs of all three operators
have been doubled. Parts (b) and (c) of Figure III-3 illustrate a comparison of the effects of changes in the probability
characteristics of operators. Part (c) is again the same as
position 0 of the location example, with one exception: the
probability characteristic of operator 2 (and only this operator) has been changed, as shown in the following table.

FIGURE PART	OPERATOR COSTS	PROBABILITY CHARACTERISTICS
a.	1 - $150.	same as shown in Chart A
	2 - 350.	"
	3 - 800.	"
b.	1 - 75.	"
	2 - 175.	"
	3 - 400.	"
c.	1 - 75.	"
	2 - 175.	shown below
	3 - 400.	same as shown in Chart A

The two different distributions for operator two are:

OPERATOR 2 m	PROBABILITY CHARACTERISTIC, $g(m)$ PARTS (a), (b)	PART (c)
-3	0	0
-2	.10	.05
-1	.25	.275
0	.30	.35
1	.25	.275
2	.10	.05

The expected costs of the several experiments, as computed, are:

EXPERIMENT	(a)	(b)	(c)
(1; 000)	7905.	7055.	7055.
(2; 000)	8181.	7270.	7318.
(3; 000)	8054.	7429.	7429.

It is seen that neither of the changes from the basic condition (b) has changed the optimality of (1; 000). Furthermore, in all three cases operator 1 is optimal at the second stage for all first-stage results of (1; 000).

Notice that in the higher-cost example (part a), the cost of operator 3 is high relative to the value of the elemental actions which it is possible to obtain. Therefore, a single use of that operator is followed by termination for all results shown (experiment (3; 000)). This implies that the optimal strategy is concerned with producing non-elemental actions, until at some point a "final plunge" is made, with the elemental operator used to produce one and only one location.

When we change the costs of operators, as in (a), the increase in cost of each experiment at the first stage will be, in general, a complex function of the costs involved. To show that the costs of the operators will enter in a complex way, we need only consider the evaluation function. Even if our evaluation were simply on the basis of one more trial, as discussed in Section 3.1, there would still be a non-linearity in the expected cost. The formula derived there is shown as

$$u^* = R + \min\left[0; \; c - \max_j \int_0^R (R-y) \; P_{ij}(y) \; dy\right].$$

FIGURE III-3   VARIATION OF OPERATOR CHARACTERISTICS

(a)

(b)

(c)

If we were to gradually increase the cost of the elemental operator, holding everything else constant, the expected cost u^* would
increase. Finally, we would reach the point at which the additional elemental experiment was no longer worth while, at which
point the utility u^* would remain constant. Instead of this one
point of non-linearity, our evaluation procedure takes into account
5 applications of the elemental operator, and so may possess a very
large number of points of non-linearity. This can be seen by examining the terminal utilities at stage 2: these are not in the
ratio of 2:1, as one might suppose from the fact that the costs
of operator 3 are in that ratio.

The expected costs of the experiments at the first stage also
illustrate this complexity; so far as we can tell, the increase
in these costs between the two sets of operator costs cannot be
related in any simple, direct way to the differences in operator
costs. The only way to explain them is in terms of a full description of the model.

We turn now to the effects of changes in the probability characteristic of operator 2. In part (b) of the figure, we see that
SLO 2 is not optimal as a 1st or 2nd stage experiment, at any
point. Furthermore, it does not enter into the evaluation formula.
Therefore, we would not expect a change in its conditional to have
much effect in the first stage, except in the expected cost of
(2; 000).

Examining (2; 000), in part (c) we find that the best experiment at the second stage is still (1; 000), independent of the
first-stage result. In most cases, the expected cost of operator 2
at the second stage (after 2 at the first stage), is increased by
amounts which reach $200. (result $9000.). The cost of operator 2

at the first stage is also increased, by about $40. The more-peaked probability characteristic produces only a slightly more-peaked distribution over the first-stage results of (2; 000).

It is not clear why increasing the peakedness of the characteristic should increase the expected cost. One explanation would be that as the "spread" of a distribution increases, results far above and below the mean become more likely, and the increased desirability of lower results outweighs the increased cost of higher results.

7. Effects of constraints on the engineer

In the most general situation, the engineer is perfectly free to perform any experiments he wishes, in any order. In practice, however, there are usually constraints which restrict the engineer's freedom of choice in some way. Such constraints can arise in several ways: the organizational environment in which the location process takes place; the influence of custom or of codified procedures; etc. We shall examine briefly four typical constraints.

To describe these constraints, we recall that at any particular stage in a location process, we have a list of all the actions generated so far. Knowing the SLO's available, we can construct a list of all those experiments which are defined (Section II-6.2). Considering this list of potential experiments, we can describe any constraint by the way in which it eliminates certain experiments from this list.

We shall discuss here four constraints. Of these, "sequence" and "jump-back" have the effect of eliminating all those experiments which involve operators of certain levels; "band-width" and "look-ahead" eliminate experiments which involve certain actions.

7.1 Sequence constraint

The choice of possible experiments might be constrained by requiring that a certain orderly progression in the use of the operators be maintained. For example, if the operator used in the last experiment was of level n, then there might be the requirement that only operators of levels $(n-1)$, (n), or $(n+1)$

FIGURE III - 4   SEQUENCE   CONSTRAINT

(a) STATUS OF THE ANALYSIS: 3 SLO'S

LIST OF ACTIONS GENERATED SO FAR

NO.	LEVEL	LABEL
4	4	000
2	3	100
3	2	110
4	3	200

LAST ACTION: 200

(b) POTENTIAL ACTIONS RESULTING FROM DIFFERENT CHOICES
OF THE NEXT EXPERIMENT:

NO.	LEVEL	LABEL	PROHIBITED BY SEQUENCE CONSTRAINT
5(i)	1	111	X
5(ii)	2	120	—
5(iii)	1	101	X
5(iv)	2	210	—
5(v)	1	201	X
5(vi)	3	300	—
5(vii)	2	010	—
5(viii)	1	001	X

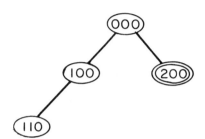

130

FIGURE III-5   JUMP-BACK CONSTRAINT

(a) STATUS OF THE ANALYSIS (3 SLO'S)

NO.	LEVEL	LABEL
1	4	.000
2	3	100
3	2	110
4	2	120

LAST ACTION GENERATED: 120

(b) POTENTIAL ACTIONS RESULTING FROM DIFFERENT CHOICES OF THE NEXT EXPERIMENT :

NO.	LEVEL	LABEL	PROHIBITED IF NO JUMP-BACK
i	1	101	—
ii	1	111	—
iii	1	121	—
iv	2	130	—
v	1	001	—
vi	2	010	—
vii	3	200	X

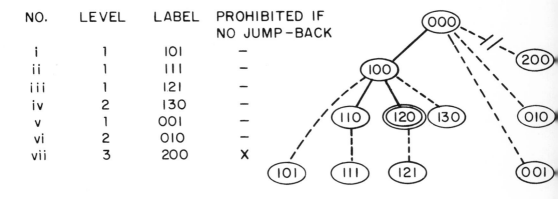

131

can be used on the next experiment: the operators of the next highest, next lowest, or same level. We identify this requirement by saying that our location process is "sequence-constrained."

For example, in the typical location process described in Section I-2, sequence is constrained because the engineer cannot skip any level in the location process, but is required to work from one level to the next.

This constraint is illustrated in Figure III-4. The sequence constraint operates by eliminating from the list of possible experiments all those which do not involve operators of levels (n-1), (n), or (n+1).

7.2   Jump-back

Like sequence, the jump-back constraint expresses a relation between the operators used on successive cycles. If the normal progression of SLO's is visualized as proceeding from the higher-level ones to those of lower level, then to "jump-back" is to reverse this: that is, to follow one SLO with another of higher level.   If jump-back is not allowed, then the only permissible experiments are those which utilize SLO's which are of the same or lower level than the one just executed.

The implication of the jump-back constraint is that, once control has been transferred from one level of analysis (SLO) to a lower level, new actions can no longer be generated at the higher levels.

This constraint is illustrated in Figure III-5.

7.3 Band-width

The band-width constraint expresses limitations on the number of actions of particular levels which might be considered actively at any particular stage of the process. For example, limited computer memory might allow us to store in the computer the terrain data for only two bands of interest. In this case, the band-width at the level corresponding to "bands of interest" has been restricted to two actions.

Let the maximum number of actions which can be retained at each level, I, be given by the subscripted variable NWIDE(I), in general different for each I. If there are more than NWIDE(I) actions of level I, then each action is evaluated with respect to some criterion - for example, the mean or mode of the prior probability for that action, or some criterion like that used in ANDREA (Section 2.2).[1] Of these actions, only the NWIDE (I) best with respect to this criterion are preserved; all others are eliminated from the list of actions (together with their included actions). Thus, there is a corresponding decrease in the number of potential experiments.

The band-width constraint is illustrated in Figure III-6.

7.4 Look-ahead

Let i be the highest level for which the analyst has actions. If N is the number of levels of look-ahead, then the analyst is permitted to look ahead to actions as far down as level (i-N), before having to choose among the actions at level i. Therefore,

_____

[1]The ANDREA criterion is the one used in GUIDE I, for simulation of the band-width constraint.

FIGURE Ⅲ-6 BAND-WIDTH CONSTRAINT

(a) STATUS:

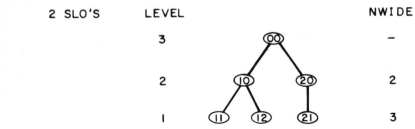

2 SLO'S	LEVEL		NWIDE
	3	⟨00⟩	—
	2	⟨10⟩ ⟨20⟩	2
	1	⟨11⟩ ⟨12⟩ ⟨21⟩	3

(b) SLO OF LEVEL 2 USED NEXT:

ORIGINAL   ALTERNATIVE FINAL RESULTS**

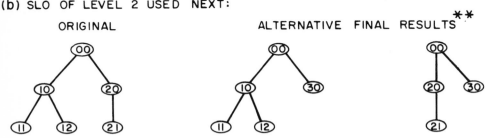

(c) SLO OF LEVEL 1 USED NEXT:

ORIGINAL   ALTERNATIVE FINAL STATES

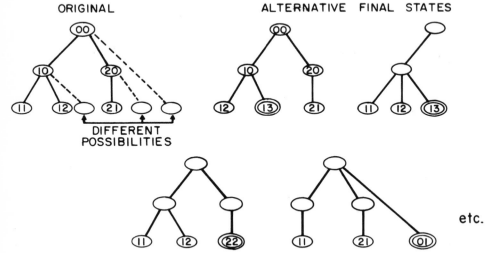

DIFFERENT
POSSIBILITIES

etc.

**NOTE THAT WHEN A PARTICULAR ACTION IS REMOVED, WE HAVE
ASSUMED HERE THAT ALL INCLUDED ACTIONS ARE ALSO REMOVED

FIGURE III-7 LOOK-AHEAD CONSTRAINT

(a) CONSTRAINTS

LOOK-AHEAD = 1 LEVEL
BANDWIDTH = ∞

STATUS

NO.	LEVEL	LABEL
1	4	000
2	3	100

(b) POTENTIAL NEXT RESULTS:

NO.	LEVEL	LABEL
3 (i)	2	110
(ii)	1	101
(iii)	3	200
(iv)	2	010
(v)	1	001

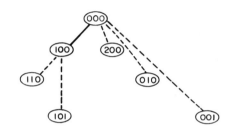

(c) TREE RESULTING AFTER APPLICATION OF LOOK-AHEAD

(i) (ii) (iii) (iv) (v)

(d) POTENTIAL RESULTS AT 2ND NEXT STAGE :

(i)

(ii) NO OTHER EXPERIMENTS POSSIBLE

(iii)

(iv)

(v) NO OTHER EXPERIMENTS POSSIBLE

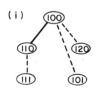
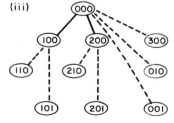
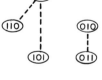

135

any experiment which uses an SLO of levels, i, i-1, ..., i-N, is permitted without any complication. As soon as an experiment is examined which requires an SLO of level (i-N-1) or lower, then the analyst must change i, the level at which he is working. This change of level is done by eliminating all the actions at level i, and all their included actions.

To summarize, any experiment of level i or lower is permitted; but, if the level of the proposed SLO is lower than (i-N), then it is necessary to make a decision about which actions to preserve at the higher levels, before advancing the analysis to a lower level.

Look-ahead is illustrated in Figure III-7.

7.5 The costs of constraints: an example

GUIDE I can be used to compute the effect of these constraints on the expected costs of different experiments, and the expected cost of the optimal experiment. In Figure III-8, we illustrate such a computation.[1]

Reading from left to right across the figure, we show five cases: (a) no constraints; (b) jump-back prohibited; (c) sequence constrained; (d) both sequence constrained and jump-back prohibited; (e) look-ahead restricted to one level and band-width restricted to two actions at each level. In this particular example, for these particular actions, priors, operator characteristics, and operator costs, we see that there is indeed a cost penalty incurred when the engineer is required to operate under these constraints.

---

[1] Chart A and Figure II-3 are both unconstrained situations.

The following is a summary of the results:

CONDITION	EXPECTED COSTS (1; 000)	(2; 100)	(3; 100)	BEST EXPERIMENT
a) Unconstrained	$7455.	7480.	7476.	(1; 000)
b) Sequence constrained	8379.	7480.	--	(2; 100)
c) Jump-back prohibited	7455.	7480.	7485.	(1; 000)
d) Sequence constrained and jump-back prohibited	8379.	7480.	--	(2; 100)
e) Look-ahead and band-width restricted	7641.	7483.	8177.	(2; 100)

Figure III-8 is based upon the same data as the example location process described above. The computations are made from position B. Position B was selected because at that point we have two
non-elemental actions, as well as (000), thus providing scope for
ANDREA to have an effect; and so the band-width constraint can
have some impact. Furthermore, a priori inspection of the tree at
B indicated that the constraints would probably have some effect.
For example, if we had used the higher operator costs, as shown in
Figure III-3 (a), the results would probably not have been so dramat
ic. As inspection of that figure shows the constraints would probably have little effect on the expected costs.

Examination of the figure or the tabulated results shows that
there is little difference in the expected costs of the experiments
at the first stage under the unconstrained condition. The maximum
difference, $25., is less than half the lowest operator cost. As
shown in Figure III-8, after either experiment (1; 000) or (3; 100),
the optimal experiment in stage 2 varies markedly; thus, we would
expect the constraints to increase the expected costs of these
first-stage experiments noticeably. The variation is less for
operator 2, and so we would expect less of an increase in the cost.

Under the condition of sequence constraint, shown in part (b), the expected cost of operator 1 increases significantly. This is because the opportunity of using operator 3 in the second stage is lost, since under this constraint operator 1 must be followed by either 1 or 2. Note that the operation of the evaluation procedure under this constraint is unsatisfactory, since operator 1 is given excessively high expected cost. Since operator 3 cannot be applied immediately following operator 1, no experiment is permitted at the third stage, in the evaluation procedure, and so the utility at that stage is R, the cost of the least-expensive elemental action found so far. In this case, R is arbitrarily high, and so the cost of operator 1 at the second stage is high also; in another case, where R had reached a reasonably low value through the production of one or more elemental actions, the error would not have been so great. Obviously, it is necessary to extend the evaluation procedure to accomodate such cases.

In the case of this particular example, we made a run with the number of stages (KSET) fixed at three. Although the costs of operator 1 at the second stage were brought down to a reasonable level (about $8500-9000), this did not affect the optimal experiment at the second stage. Therefore, increasing the number of stages by one did not change the results at the first stage significantly. (The change was actually a decrease of 0.3% in the cost of the best experiment.)

We see further that operator 3 is not examined, as a first-stage experiment, because of the sequence constraint. The expected cost of operator 2 is completely unchanged, and in fact 2 becomes the optimal experiment, since the expected cost of operator 1 has so increased. Therefore, we get only the one shot, and so our expected cost is high.

a) UNCONSTRAINED

Considering operator 2, we see that we lose the opportunity of using operator 1, henceforth, because we have had to eliminate the action at level 4, (000). This also affects the experiments using operators 2 and 3 at the second stage, since we lose the opportunity of applying these operators to action (000). (There is one peculiarity which we have not yet explained satisfactorily: for results 6000. and 7000. the cost of the experiment at the second stage is less when restricted to (100), then when we had the freedom to elect (000). This may arise from the ANDREA criterion. This definitely needs further investigation.)

To anticipate the effects of the jump-back constraint, we could look at the unconstrained case in part (a). Operator 1 will be unaffected because any experiment at the second stage will be permissible under this constraint, following 1. Operator 2 would be affected only if operator 1 were optimal in the second stage, but this does not happen in this example. We do expect operator 3 to be affected, since results 8000. and 9000. do have operators 1 and 2 as optimal experiments for the second stage. However, the effect will be small, since the expected costs of these second-stage optimal experiments are not very different from the costs of the experiments which will be permitted under the constraint. Finally, we note that the evaluation procedure will not be affected by the jump-back constraint, since only operator 3 is involved in it. These arguments explain in full the results observed in part (c) of the figure, where only the expected cost of operator 3 is increased from the unconstrained condition.

We turn now to part (d) of the figure, where we have the effects of both sequence constraint and a prohibition on jump-back. (This is very close to the condition in the typical route location process outlined in Chapter I.) This condition amounts to the overlay of both the constituent constraints, in that the experiments removed from consideration are those removed by either one constraint or the other or both. Operator 1 is affected only by the sequence constraint aspect, and so we find it has the same expected costs as under that condition. Since neither constraint separately affected operator 2, we find that expected cost unchanged here also. Note that there are some second-stage options removed, for experiment (2; 100) at the first stage, by the influence of the jump-back constraint. But as pointed out above, since these are not optimal, their removal has no effect on the expected costs at the first stage. Operator 3 is prohibited by the sequence constraint.

In part (e) of the figure we show a case of look-ahead and band-width constraints. The number of levels of look-ahead is restricted to one; and the band-width is restricted to two actions at each level.

The action of band-width and the look-ahead constraint together, requires that once we use operator 3, we must eliminate all actions at level 3, and all except two of the actions at level 2. So, in our example, if we go directly to operator 3 we find that we are at a dead end, because we have had to eliminate all the actions at levels 4 and 3, and there are none at level 2. There are further effects beyond, in the increased costs for the results 8000. and 9000. following (2; 100), and also for all results following operator 1 at stage one. These increases are directly attributable to the way in which these

140

constraints reduce the engineer's flexibility, by eliminating some actions from which it may be desirable under certain conditions to produce an elemental action.

8. Comments on the present implementation of the model

The present version of GUIDE I is not a production program. From the point of view of demonstrating the computational feasibility of our model, it is strictly experimental, for these reasons:

1. The program is written in FORTRAN, a language which is convenient for programming but which is less efficient than a language closer to machine level, like FAP. Furthermore, FORTRAN is basically for algebraic computations, whereas some other language, such as LISP, may be more appropriate for tree-search computations.

2. The present program is implemented in the Compatible Time-Sharing System (CTSS) now being used experimentally at M.I.T. (based upon an IBM 7094 computer). In the current version of this system, programs written in FORTRAN are first translated into the MAD language by MADTRAN, and then compiled. Such MAD-compiled programs will generally run slower than direct FORTRAN compilations.[1]

3. When doing the actual programming, our primary objective was to get the program operational as rapidly as possible. An important secondary objective was for the program to be understandable to potential users. Therefore, running efficiency, storage efficiency, and general programming elegance were very much tertiary objectives.

4. The heuristics used in GUIDE I are relatively simple and direct.

---

[1] Memorandum CC-181-2, Computation Center, M.I.T., Cambridge, Massachusetts (August 1963).

142

For a particular problem, the major factors controlling the computer time are: the parameters which control the maximum number of stages and the minimum probability of a result; the KSET and PRBMN criteria; and the number of SLO's available, the constraints (cf. Section 7), and the number of classes over which the probability distributions are described. (In the examples in this chapter, we used 12 classes, each with a width of $1000.) It is not possible at this time to give any general rules for approximating the running time of a given problem. However, for the examples shown, the actual IBM 7094 time used was about twenty to thirty minutes for two stages, and about four hours for three stages.

Because of these running times, we were forced to restrict our experimental runs to two stages. Only in a few instances did we run a problem with KSET equal to three to check certain situations (e.g., the constraints).

In spite of its limitations, we feel that the program does produce interesting results. In this sense, the model is computationally feasible. Also, it is versatile: our experiments have illustrated the exploration of a number of interesting issues beyond the basic question of which experiment to do next.

However, these experiments have also shown up a number of limitations and peculiarities in the program's behavior. Furthermore, it certainly is necessary to test whether the results we obtain for KSET = 2 are similiar to those we would obtain with KSET = 10 or 20. If such tests show that the results of runs with two stages are reasonably good indicators of the optimal experiment, then the present GUIDE I can be considered to demonstrate the computational feasibility of the model.

We suspect that this will not be true. In that case, further research and a major reprogramming effort would be required, to develop additional, more powerful heuristics, and a better computer program. The objective would be to achieve greater accuracy by a more subtle and thorough exploration of the tree, at reasonable expense in machine time. To achieve this, a major investigation of the effects of different approximations and heuristics, in different problem types, would be necessary.

In Section 2.10 of the next chapter, we give several approaches which we think are worth consideration, as possible heuristics.

To summarize: The present computer program is not a production program: there are many difficulties with it, particularly its running time, and there are still questions about the accuracy of the computations. Clearly, much further work needs to be done.

However, this experiment has had value: we have shown how the model might be used in the stage-by-stage analysis of a particular location process, and our two other examples illustrate the potential variety of analyses for which this model might be useful. We hope that these experiments, as preliminary as they are, still suggest the wide variety of avenues for further research in this general topic of models for guiding engineering processes.

In the next chapter, we suggest some possible directions for further work, and also summarize briefly what we consider to be the more important implications of this research.

CHAPTER IV

SUMMARY, IMPLICATIONS, AND EXTENSIONS

The main subject of this chapter is the implications of our model of a location process. We begin the chapter with a summary of the model. Then, using this summary as a base, we make a number of brief comments on the assumptions in the model, the implications of the model, and potential directions for extending it. Finally, in the third section we comment on the implications of this work for the design of the man-machine system for highway location, now under development at M.I.T.

1. Summary of the model

1.1 General Description

The engineer has available for solving a given problem two or more Single-Level Operators. Each operator consists of procedures for generating an action, for predicting the consequences of the action, for evaluating those consequences, and for determining the cost of that action.

Each operator generates actions of a characteristic kind. For example, in highway location we have operators concerned with bands of interest; with alignments; with profiles; etc.

Actions produced by one operator can be compared with those produced by another operator. We say that action A _includes_ action B if action A can be interpreted as a set of actions like B. (This is more precisely expressed through the concept of a metric.) If the actions produced by operator N characteristically are included in actions produced by operator M, then we say that operator M is of higher level than operator N. The level relation yields an ordering over the set of operators available to the engineer.

That operator which is of the lowest level of the set is the only one which produces actions that can be considered to be solutions to the particular problem. We call the actions produced by this operator "elemental" actions. We assume that the cost of an elemental action is determined with certainty by the selection part of that operator.

We call the actions produced by any other operators "non-elemental" actions; these can be interpreted as sets of elemental actions. One particular non-elemental action is the universal action, or set of all elemental actions.

An experiment is defined as the application of an operator to an action which was produced previously (or the universal action) to yield another action. The new action is of lower level than the action from which it was produced, and included in it. A highway location process can be described as the execution of a series of such experiments.

Each time the engineer executes an experiment he incurs a cost. The action resulting from an experiment, and its cost, are uncertain. Our objective is to determine, at any point in the location process, which experiment is the best one to do next, considering the possible results of the experiment and the cost of executing it.

We have developed a model to be used to determine the best experiment to do next. This model uses Bayesian decision theory. We assume that the engineer can place a subjective probability distribution over each non-elemental action which he has generated previously; this functions as a "prior" distribution.

We also assume that each Single-Level Operator is characterized by a conditional probability distribution. For a given experiment, the probability distribution over the possible costs of the action produced is obtained from the prior distribution over the action to which the operator is to be applied, and the conditional distribution for that operator. The observed result of the experiment is the cost of the action produced; given this result, the prior distributions over one or more non-elemental actions (chosen according to certain rules) are revised according to Bayes Theorem.

If the operator used was the one of lowest level, then the action produced is elemental, and a possible solution to the problem. If some other operator was used then the action produced is non-elemental; no solution has been gained, but possibly the engineer has improved his prospects of ultimately obtaining a solution.

In choosing among possible experiments to do next, the objective is to balance the cost of doing an experiment against the returns, as reflected in terms of getting solutions less costly than the best found so far. With the probabilistic model described, an expected-value criterion is used to determine the best experiment.

The computations required to actually determine the best experiment are performed by computer. The program utilizes several simple heuristics to do this computation.

1.2 The model: normative procedure

At any point in the problem-solving process, the DM has A, the set of actions a_j which he has produced so far. Given the set of operators 0_i in his repertory, the DM has a choice of experiments e_{ij} (all permissible combinations of operators and actions), and the additional option of terminating the process, denoted by e_o.

If he elects to terminate, the payoff is the utility of the best elemental action found so far. If he executes an experiment, he incurs the cost of using the operator, but gains the possibility of (a) producing, or (b) getting information which may lead ultimately to producing, an elemental action more desirable than the best found so far.

The problem is not which action to choose, for the choice of an elemental action to implement is determined by its (known) utility. Rather, the choice is among experiments: i.e., which procedure (operator), if any, to use next for producing another action, or whether to terminate.

When an operator i is used to produce an action, the DM incurs a fixed cost, c_i.

An experiment e_{ij} is the application of operator i to action j, to produce an included action k and an associated estimate y_k. The cost c_i incurred by the DM depends only upon the operator used. (The operator i must be of lower level than the operator which produced j.)

150

We use the framework of Bayesian Decision Theory. Prior distributions $f_j(\theta)$ are used to characterize actions, while the conditional distributions $g_i(y \mid \theta)$ characterize the operators. Each experiment e_{ij} is characterized by a marginal $P_{ij}(y)$, where

$$P_{ij}(y) = \int_\theta g_i(y \mid \theta) \; f_j(\theta) \; d\theta \quad .$$

Let the state of the location process, S, be defined as: F, the set of distributions $f_j(\theta)$ for all the non-elemental actions produced so far, and R, the utility of the most desirable elemental action so far produced -- S = S (R,F). We need a set of rules for predicting how S changes to S' as a result of executing an experiment e_{ij} and observing the result, the index y of the action produced: S' = S' (S,e_{ij},y). We also need a utility function, U (S), which represents the value of being in a particular state S. Then we consider each possible experiment e_{ij} and each possible result y; compute the change in state to S' and the corresponding U (S'), consequent upon e_{ij} and y; take the expected value via $P_{ij}(y)$; and incorporate the cost of the experiment c_i. The optimal experiment e^* is that e_{ij} (including termination, e_o) for which the net expected utility, U_{ij} is the greatest, U^*:

$$U^* = \underset{ij}{\mathrm{Max}} \left\{ \int_{ij}(y) \; U \; \left[S'(S,e_{ij},y) \right] \; dy \; - \; c_i \right\}$$

A detailed description follows.

Priors

For every non-elemental action j, there is a distribution $h_j(u)$ over the utilities, u, of locations included in j. This represents the true, or actual distribution of utilities; but the engineer is more interested in the distribution of what he would get if he were to apply the elemental operator to action j some number of times n. Since the engineer can estimate neither of these distributions directly, we ask him for a subjective judgment of the following form:

> For non-elemental action j, assume the elemental operator is applied some large number of times n.[1] The frequency distribution of utilities of the n elemental actions produced is denoted by some distribution $H_j(u \mid \theta)$, where θ is some parameter of this distribution (mean, median, lowest decile, least of the n values, etc.). We ask the DM to give his judgment about values of θ, as $f_j(\theta)$.

For example, if θ is the least of the n values, then $f_j(\theta)$ is the DM's judgmental distribution over the utility of the most desirable elemental action in a large number of operator applications.

Conditionals

Each operator i is characterized by a conditional distribution $g_i(y \mid \theta)$, defined thus: given that action j is characterized by a distribution $H_j(u \mid \theta)$ with $\theta = \theta_o$, then $g_i(y \mid \theta_o)$ is the probability that application of operator i will produce an action with index equal to y.

---

[1] The number n is required only to be greater than any reasonably likely number of operator applications, so that θ serves as a reference point that is never actually attained.

These distributions g_i measure, essentially, the relative amounts of information supplied by different operators. A small variance will represent a good estimator, in that the value of y is a good indicator of the utility of the best elemental action which would be found in a long series of applications of the elemental operator to the action produced by e_{ij}. A skewed distribution will correspond to an operator with systematic bias; for example, consistent overoptimism in preliminary analyses using the highest-level operator.

State of the Process

At any given point in a problem-solving process, the relevant information is: the list of all the actions generated so far, with (a) the current probability distribution $f_j(\theta)$ for each non-elemental action and the utility r_j for each elemental action, and (b) a representation of the inclusion relationships among all the actions, such as the tree diagram shown in Figure I-3, or some more compact notation. Of particular interest are R = max (r_j), and F, the set of $f_j(\theta)$; we define the state S = (R,F).

Changes in State of the Process

When an experiment e_{IJ} is performed and the index value for the resulting action, k, is y, the following changes in the state S take place:

(1) The new action k is added to the list of actions
(2) Some or all $f_j(\theta)$ change as a result of the information in y
(3) If the new action k is elemental, R = max (r_j) may change

The rules for predicting the new distribution $f''_j(\theta)$ from the old one, $f'_j(\theta)$, for all j are based on Bayes Theorem, modified to reflect the hierarchical structure:

(1)   if k is included in j,

$$f''_j(\theta) = \frac{f_j'(\theta)\; g_I(y\mid\theta)}{\int_\theta f_j'(\theta)\; g_I(y\mid\theta)\; d\theta}$$

(2)   if k is not included in j,

$$f_j''(\theta) = f_j'(\theta)$$

(3)   for action k

$f_k''(\theta) = f_J''(\theta)$, where J is the "parent" action on which operator I was used.

A detailed motivation for these rules is given on pages 64-78. Roughly, these rules imply the following picture: no matter how many locations (not yet generated) it may contain, a non-elemental action from which no lower-level actions have been produced is assumed homogeneous -- until he generates an included action, the DM has no basis for differentiating between different parts of the non-elemental action. As a consequence, the prior over the new action is the same as the prior over the "parent" (the action from which it is generated), and so the posteriors $f_j''(\theta)$ are identical too. However, as soon as another action is generated which is included within the parent, the parent and the first included actions start going their own paths, in that the distributions change differently. For example, if action a has just been generated from action b, then $f_a(\theta) = f_b(\theta)$. Now, if c is also generated from b, then $f''_c(\theta) = f''_b(\theta) \neq f_b(\theta)$ but $f_a(\theta)$ remains unchanged.

Utility Function

For any state $S(R,F)$, the simplest assumption is that $U(S) = R$. This corresponds to assuming that the best experiment will be immediate termination, so that the value of the state is the utility of the best location found so far; the value of future prospects, information which is carried in the distribution $f_j(\theta)$, is ignored.

This is patently a poor assumption in most situations, at least for states near to the present one. However, if one looks at possible states 20 experiments into the future, it is not clear that the bias involved in evaluating those future states in this way is significant by the time the decision-tree computations are brought back to the immediate next states. This, in fact, is roughly the approach we have taken in practical computations:[1] we construct a decision tree going a number of experiments into the future, make an assumption of this type, and work back with the expected-value calculations to the best experiment for the next stage.

---

[1]
 Cf. Chapter 3.

2. Discussion: Assumptions, implications, and extensions of this research

The comments in the following sections are arranged roughly in the sequence in which the summary of the model in Section I touches upon them.

2.1 Highway location as an example

Clearly, the discussion in this thesis could just as well be applied to other areas of engineering, planning, or management decision-making. Highway location has been selected as an example to demonstrate these ideas, first, because of the ease with which the hierarchical structure of location problems can be visualized, and second, because of the author's conviction that research in transportation planning will require and will stimulate the development of an integrated operational decision-making theory.[1]

2.2 The nature of search and selection

Search and selection procedures in an engineering process may be informal, as most present procedures in a location process are, involving mostly "engineering judgment," or they may be formal, perhaps expressed in the form of computer programs. Our model suggests that there is no a priori reason to discriminate against one or another form of procedure. From the point of view of this model, the important characteristics of search and selection procedures are their costs per application, their probability characteristics (expressing the information they yield to the engineer), and their relative levels.

---

[1]
For a discussion showing the generality of the ideas presented here, see James C. Emery, "The planning process and its formalization in computer models," in Proceedings of the Second Congress on the Information System Sciences, to be published by Spartan Press.

The approach of this model demonstrates that even if the operators in an engineering system are a mixture of completely formalized algorithms (e.g., linear programming), computer-aided procedures, and intuitive methods, we can still develop rational procedures for controlling the progress of the system toward the ultimate goal of a solution.

2.3   The assumption that the operators to be used are known

A more general problem than the one studied here is how to determine what operators should be constructed for a particular problem-solving process. One way of looking at this question is to ask, what should be the succession of metrics with which we deal as we progress from higher levels to the final solution? In terms of the set of elemental actions, we see that we are asking how we should build up aggregations of elemental actions into sets, or non-elemental actions. As our model here suggests, we probably would desire metrics such that there is a high degree of similarity among the actions included in one non-elemental action, but a high degree of difference between non-elemental actions.[1]

----

[1] The underlying issue here is complex. There is one language in which we naturally describe actions, and there is another which expresses our evaluations of those actions. Our natural tendency is to aggregate actions within the frame of reference provided by the descriptor language. But in order to get high similarity among actions, we want to aggregate them with regard to the evaluation language. The work of Christopher Alexander (NOTES ON THE SYNTHESIS OF FORM. Cambridge, Massachusetts: Harvard University Press (1964)) can be described as a way of developing new descriptor languages such that there is greater correspondence between the descriptor and evaluation languages. In our terms, such a reworking of the descriptor language would yield a new metric, or set of metrics, on the action space.

2.4 Selection places a cost on an action

We consider the model presented here as very restricted, because it assumes that every action has a "cost," or can be evaluated by some other single cardinal measure of value (in particular, a Von-Neuman Morgenstern utility).[1] Further, it assumes that the cost of an experiment is measured along the same scale. These assumptions are necessary in order to apply Bayesian decision theory as currently formulated.

We think that it will prove possible to extend this model with this assumption relaxed. The first step would be to define selection as the determination of a preference ordering over actions of the same level. Then, the probability distribution over the results of an experiment would be replaced by the probability that a new action would fall into the several different positions of the preference ordering.

2.5 Level relations among the operators in the set available

We have assumed (Section II-2.3) that the level relation exists between all pairs of operators available to the engineer. The basic logic of our model is easily extended to the case where this assumption does not hold. The only problems we foresee are in generalizing (a) the labelling notation and (b) the algorithm for determining whether an (operator, action) combination is meaningful (Section II-6.2). These should not be difficult to resolve.

_____

[1] Luce, R. Duncan, and Howard Raiffa, GAMES AND DECISIONS: New York: John Wiley and Sons (1957). Chapter 2.

2.6 There is only one operator which produces "solutions"; or, the role of models in a problem-solving process

The objective of the process is a solution, and solutions can only be produced by the lowest-level operator. This does not mean that other operators are without value. On the contrary, _every_ operator has a potential role in the problem-solving process. To determine this role, we need to look at each operator with regard to its relationship to the elemental operator; and it is only after we perform the type of calculation represented by GUIDE I that we can determine exactly the role of a particular non-elemental operator in a specific problem.

To understand the implications of this formulation, let us focus on the prediction components of our operators. We shall use the term "model" in this context to denote any procedure for predicting the physical, or real, consequences of any action. Now, a fairly typical problem in many areas of engineering and social science is the question, which of several models to use. For example, in regional planning we might have a choice between an input-output type model, and a "naive" model expressed in a single equation;[1] in urban planning we similarly have choices between different models for predicting the intra-metropolitan distribution of land use;[2] or for predicting the trips made between pairs of points in a region.[3]

---

[1] Rey, Guido, and C.B. Tilanus, "Input-output forecasts for the Netherlands, 1949-1958, ECONOMETRICA, 31:3, (July, 1963). pp. 454-463.

[2] Traffic Research Corporation, unpublished reports on EMPIRIC and POLIMETRIC, two models for use by Boston Regional Planning Project for predicting land use in the Boston region. (1964).

[3] Martin, B.V. et al. PRINCIPLES AND TECHNIQUES FOR PREDICTING FUTURE DEMAND FOR URBAN AREA TRANSPORTATION. Research Report R63-1, Cambridge, Massachusetts: Civil Engineering Systems Laboratory, M.I.T. (1963). p. 126.

From our point of view, there is not necessarily a single "best" model. Considering that each such model corresponds to the prediction component of a Single-Level Operator, we see that the real issue is, what should be the respective roles of each kind of model in solving the particular decision problem at hand. The basic choice is among actions; each model has value only to the extent to which it helps the engineer to make this choice. Interestingly, this is a direct expression of the Bayesian point of view, in which it is argued that information is of value primarily with relevance to a specific decision problem.

The Bayesian decision theory model presented here attempts to give a rational procedure for determining the relative roles of several "models" in a particular problem. Removing from our arguments the veil of route location, we can see the following procedure suggested for any problem, in which the analyst is willing to meet the condition of a single measure of value (dollars here):

1. Enumerate the models which are to be considered for possible use in this problem.
2. Define the full set of Single-Level Operators of which these models are the prediction components. This requires establishing the search, evaluation, and decision procedures to be used with each model; these may be formal or informal.
3. By comparing the Single-Level Operators, and the characteristic ways in which the actions with which they deal are described, determine the relative levels of the operators.
4. Determine the cost per application of each operator.

5. Establish one or more priors for the particular problem, and determine the conditionals for each operator, either directly, or indirectly through estimation of the posteriors, as described in Section II-3.5.

6. Use GUIDE I or a similar procedure to determine the best experiment to do; the series of such determinations will indicate for the particular problem which operators (and, thus, models) have useful roles in the process of solving the particular problem.

2.7 Assumption that the cost of an elemental action is known with certainty

Relaxation of this assumption could go in several directions:

a) explicit introduction of sensitivity analysis

In a sensitivity analysis, we explore the sensitivity of the costs of two (or more) actions to variation in the variable(s) about whose values we are uncertain.[1] If for example we are uncertain about the cost per cubic yard to use for earthwork, in comparing two bands of interest, we might let this unit cost vary over the range we consider likely. If one band is preferred to the other no matter what the value of cost, so long as in this range, then the uncertainty in this cost is not significant. On the other hand, if the preference order over the bands does depend upon the value of this unit cost (over the range of uncertainty), then for purposes of further analysis the two bands could be considered as one: the engineer is unable to discriminate between them. However, the actions of lower level generated within these actions will be the subject of investigation themselves, and will only be lumped together when

----

[1] Manheim, Marvin L., "Data accuracy in route location," TRAFFIC QUARTERLY, January, 1961.

sensitivity analysis fails to distinguish among them, too.

b) use of probability distributions over the variables which are uncertain

This immediately requires the introduction of another type of operator, different from the Single-Level Operator: namely, Data Acquisition. This has the form with which we are more usually familiar in Bayesian decision theory: it is an experiment designed to acquire information only (as opposed to experiments which also yield actions), and so can be introduced into our structure in a relatively straightforward manner.[1]

As a corollary to the introduction of the Data-acquisition operator, we must also consider actions which are defined with respect to time. We must then include an implementation operator as well: the option of implementing in the real world some part of a time-dependent action, so as to acquire information about uncertainties, the relative desirabilities of the actions, etc.

2.8 The objective: to determine the best experiment to do next

The implication of this is that we do not hope to achieve an optimum solution, but we do want to achieve an optimum process for finding solutions. In such a process, we try to find as good a solution as possible, balancing the prospects of improving the

_____

[1]Cf. Schlaifer, op.cit.; Raiffa and Schlaiffer, op.cit.

solution against the expenditures of engineering resources required to do so.

We think that the homogeneity assumption (Section II-5.3) is the part of our model which is most crucial in enabling us to develop a procedure for finding the optimum solution process. The essence of this assumption is that until the engineer has explicitly identified and demarcated some subset of actions by the execution of search at some level, he has no basis for differentiating actions in that subset from actions in its least including subset. Therefore, we make the priors over the subset and its least including action identical.

2.9 Assumption that the operator characteristic is constant

We have assumed that the engineer is able to predict how his prior will change for a specified experimental result, and that the probability characteristic of the operator is independent of the action to which it is applied. Further, we have assumed that the act of search itself results in a prior over the new action, which is the same as the one over its parent.

A more general formulation would go something like this:
a) Let $h(c|\beta_j)$ be the distribution of costs of elemental actions included within action j; β_j is the value of the parameter which specifies this distribution for action j.[1] For elemental actions, the value of β is such that the distribution is an impulse.

---

[1] For example, h may denote a normal distribution of costs; β might then correspond to the two-dimensional vector with the mean and variance of the distribution as components.

b) Represent the operation of search probabilistically. Let β_m be the value of the parameter of the distribution for the new action, m. Let α_i be a parameter which characterizes the search procedures of operator i. Then, for experiment e_{ij}, we can represent the probability that the new action is characterized by a parameter value β_m as:

$$g(\beta_m | \beta_j, \alpha_i).$$

This removes the restriction that the prior over a new action is identical to the prior over the parent.

c) The selection operation yields a value of the cost index y_m for the next action. Consider explicitly that we do not know the exact relationship of this index to the distribution $h(c | \beta_m)$. Let γ_i be a parameter which characterizes the selection operation of operator i. Then, for experiment e_{ij}, we can represent the probability that selection produces a value y_m for the new action, characterized by a parameter value β_m, as:

$$f(y_m | \beta_m, \gamma_i).$$

d) Now, instead of expressing our priors directly in terms of costs and holding the operator characteristics constant, we can place priors over actions, in the form of distributions $P(\beta_j)$, and over operator characteristics as $P(\alpha_i, \gamma_i)$. When we observe the result of an experiment as y_m, we can proceed to revise these priors by Bayes Theorem, using the functions f, g, and h.

164

With this kind of model, we would be able to acquire information about operator characteristics as well as subsets of the action domain. This would be a very interesting kind of learning, in which the total problem solving system would "learn" from problem to problem (about γ_i, α_i), and within a given problem (about the β_j's).

2.10 Heuristics for implementing the computation

In the present implementation of GUIDE I, we have barely begun to explore the subtleties of improving the computational feasibility of our Bayesian decision theory model. There seems at this point to be a necessity to increase significantly the accuracy of the computation without increasing the computing cost.

We summarize briefly a few of our thoughts which may be useful in this respect.

Modification of present evaluation procedure

The evaluation procedure currently implemented is based upon one additional stage after KSET with information change, and four stages additional without information change (Section III-3.3). This procedure should be generalized, with two parameters, one each to specify the number of stages for each of these segments of the calculation. Then, a decision rule should be formulated to set these parameters such that the number of stages with and without information change is a function of the probability of the experimental result at the termination point.

A third option can be introduced into this evaluation procedure: revise the prior for each result of the elemental experiments, but do not bother with any of the other status updating
operations (except, of course, the revision of the best elemental
action found so far). This would be intermediate in computing
time between the two procedures outlined; it would be less than
the KSET procedure because the revised priors would be computed
for only the one action, and ANDREA would not be used.

Evaluation function

Postulate some form of function which gives the value of
the terminal position as some algebraic (or other) function of
(i) the value of the best elemental action found to that point;
(ii) one or more parameters of the probability distributions
over the actions available at that point (e.g., F(R) and EPROB
as used in ANDREA - cf. Section III-2); (iii) the cost of the
Single-Level Operator for elemental actions; (iv) the stage of
the terminal point in the tree, etc.

This function can be estimated _a priori_ and kept constant
throughout the evaluation of the decision tree; it can be
derived from data obtained from the analysis of past decision
trees; or it itself can be left variable and treated in a
Bayesian manner. For example, let the variables be incorporated in a linear equation, with the coefficients to be determined. A prior distribution is placed over the coefficients,
and the mean values used for making decisions. However, each
time that the tracing of a tree passes through a node, not
terminating there, the actual, computed value of the return
at that node can be compared with the value that would be
obtained if the node were a terminal node and the evaluation

formula applied. The observed differences can then be used to compute a posterior distribution over the weights in the evaluation function. In this way, a successively better formula can be obtained for evaluating terminal positions.[1]

The determination of appropriate terms to use in any evaluation of a terminal position is very difficult. At present, it seems to us that the implications of the status of the process at a point are very subtle and complex, in that the "true" (i.e., most accurate estimate obtainable) utility of a position is in general a very intricate function of the distributions over the various actions, the number of actions, etc. For instance, the relationship between the various operator costs and the variances of the priors will significantly affect the type of evaluation procedure which gives the best results; but this relationship will be difficult to express.

Consistency of evaluation

Schlaiffer[2] outlines a flexible pruning rule which illustrates the potential of explicit interdependence of pruning rules and evaluation formulas. The procedure suggested is as follows: using the evaluation formula, determine valuations for a set of potential termination points, all at the same stage. Working backwards, compute the best decision for the first stage. Next, trace out the tree several stages further than for the previous

---

[1] Similar ideas are described in Samuel, A.L., "Some studies in machine learning using the game of checkers," in Feigenbaum, Edward A., and Julian Feldman, COMPUTERS AND THOUGHT. New York: McGraw-Hill (1963), pp. 71-105.

[2] Schlaiffer, op.cit., p. 601

calculation, apply the same evaluation formula to evaluate the new terminal points, and working backwards, determine if the same decisions would be made at the previous stages. If so, computation ceases; if not, then computation continues, and the tree is traced out for several stages further, when the test is again performed.

Repertory of evaluation procedures

Develop a series of evaluation procedures. Determine their relative costs in machine time, and accuracy (approximate). At a given terminal position, apply the quickest procedure first; then work back one stage and determine the expected costs of the experiments at that previous stage:

1. If the difference in expected cost between the best experiment and the next best one is greater than a criterion value, accept the evaluations; if not, go back to the terminal position and try the next most costly evaluation procedure.

or:

2. Apply both the least-costly and second-least costly procedures. Compare the results. If the difference is greater than a criterion amount, repeat using the next-most-costly procedure; if less, accept some function (average, etc.) of the estimates and continue tracing the tree.

Other ways of utilizing a repertory of evaluation procedures are the suggestion of Schlaiffer, cited above, and Fleisher's suggestion, as described in the footnote to the PRBMN criterion in Section III-2.

An optimism criterion

Apply several procedures to evaluate a terminal position, and use the most optimistic of the resulting scores. Alternatives are: a weighted average; a pessimism criterion, etc. (The weighted average is not identical to the evaluation polynomial approach if at least one of the evaluation procedures looks beyond the present stage.)

Check for termination condition

It will probably be useful to distinguish the condition when the value of the best elemental action found so far is such as to make stopping a reasonable possibility, from otherwise. It is important to have a pruning rule which will prevent waste computation under this condition.

For instance, given a result at a particular stage, and the consequent updating of the status, use a very approximate evaluation procedure to determine which experiments are better than stopping. If there is none, then tree-tracing ceases at that branch. A final evaluation of the position is made with one of the more powerful evaluation procedures. If some experiment is better than stopping, then tree-tracing continues.

"Sufficient statistics" formulations

The extensive work of Raiffa and Schlaiffer[1] suggests the possibility that a major computational reduction may be achieved by using their "sufficient statistics" formulation, with the use of standardized probability distributions, such as the normal,

_____

[1] op.cit.

binomial, or Poisson. We rejected this approach in designing
GUIDE I, and used instead a discrete distribution of general
form. We think our reasons for this are still valid, and that
adoption of this approach would not improve computational time.

Our reasons for this rejection were, first, that each of
these standard distribution forms corresponds to a very particular model of the underlying probabilistic process, and so use
of one of these, without specific theoretical justification,
introduces some very serious biases into the model. As an
extreme example, the use of a normal prior and normal conditional would result in the undesirable condition that successive observations on the same action reduced the variance of
the prior, no matter how scattered the observations were.[1]

The second reason for this rejection was that we did not
think there would be a significant saving in computational time.
Time would be saved in computing the posteriors, obviously, but
the actual computation of the posterior distribution is a very
small part of the total computational time (a guess would put
it at between 5% and 0.5%). Against this slight gain, there
would be countered the necessity for extensive table-look-up
procedures or else some significant computation for obtaining
particular values of the probabilities, partial expectations,
etc.

Concluding comment on heuristics:

Developing improved procedures for shortening the computations on a logical basis (as opposed to programming innovations)
is going to be a very difficult task. It will take careful and

------
[1] op.cit., p.295.

extensive study of the behavior of decision-tree computations
under a variety of problem conditions. We do not think that
generalizations will appear readily; rather, the approach
will definitely have to be one of trial-and-error.

Underlying the basic complexity of the problem, there
will also be this methodological issue: how to tell whether
one set of heuristics is better than another. The definition
of "accuracy" which we gave in Section III-5.4 will probably
be useful only as a first approximation.

2.11 Implications of time-sharing

GUIDE I is presently available in the form of a IBM 7094
program, written in FORTRAN and FAP, and compiled and operational
on the M.I.T. Compatible Time-Sharing System.[1] For experimenta-
tion with the program, CTSS is very useful, in that the analyst
can observe the program's performance as it computes, immediately
making any necessary adjustments.

Perhaps the best way to decide which heuristics to use under
a given set of circumstances is to let the engineer make the decisions as the computations evolve. If so, time-sharing is one way
of achieving this. The program would be designed for engineer
intervention at any point in the computations; the engineer
would interrupt, set some switches to control the heuristics
selection, and resume computation or go back to some selected
position in the computations.

---

[1] M.I.T. Computation Center, THE COMPATIBLE TIME-SHARING SYSTEM:
A PROGRAMMER'S GUIDE. Cambridge, Massachusetts: The M.I.T.
Press (1963).

If GUIDE I is implemented in the context of some integrated
time-shared system such as the proposed system for route location (see next section), then this program should certainly have
the ability to run in time-sharing. Probably GUIDE should be
run in the background of the computations (although controlled
from the foreground system) because of the length of the computations, while in the foreground the engineer is actually running
those programs associated with a particular Single-Level Operator.
Run in this fashion, GUIDE would be used to compute the optimal
next experiment contingent on the result of the experiment which
the operator is executing in the foreground. With appropriate
timing and control logic, perhaps the GUIDE computation could be
controlled by the nature of the operator in the foreground, to
finish its computation about the same time that the engineer
observes the result of the Single-Level Operator and is ready
to go on to the next experiment; the heuristics used by GUIDE
would be selected to achieve the maximum accuracy in the available computational time.

2.12 "Validity" of the model

This model is not descriptive, but prescriptive.

We do not argue that our model of the location process
mirrors the actual thought processes of the engineer. If we
were to make such a claim, then we would have to compare the
actual information state of the engineer after the execution
of an experiment, with that we predicted from our model; we
would have to compare the choice of experiment made by the
engineer with that which our model recommends; and we would
have to explain any differences.

Such comparisons are irrelevant, because we are not attempting to replace the engineer. Rather, we are trying to improve his control of his problem, by outlining for him a framework in which he can organize his decisions. We are prescribing a procedure for him to follow, not describing his usual approach. This is an important difference, because the success of our formulation should rest, not on arguments or comparisons, but on each engineer's willingness to adapt his own personal mode of operation to the framework of our model.

3. Implications for the design of a route location system

At the Civil Engineering Systems Laboratory at M.I.T. there is currently underway a major research effort to design an integrated man-machine system for transportation planning. The first phase implementation of this system will focus primarily on the route location problem, in the rural context, as we have described it here.[1]

One useful way to explore the implications of the subject of this thesis is in the context of designing this system:

1. There should be explicit recognition of the fact that route location is a hierarchically-structured process. That is, there should be available to the engineer a number of Single-Level Operators, at a variety of levels. This requires that the procedures for handling terrain data and other information must be explicitly organized to facilitate the engineer's ability to move freely from one level of analysis to another.

   This point of view is also extremely important in indicating the general outlines of the location system. There are an increasing number of programs and procedures available which have some degree of relevance to the location problem. The framework provided by this theory of hierarchical structure helps us to understand the relationships among these new programs, and how they fit into an integrated location system, by focussing on their levels, whether they are search or selection procedures, how they

---

[1] Roberts, Paul O., Manheim, Marvin L., and Suhrbier, John H. A MAN-MACHINE SYSTEM FOR SOLVING HIGHWAY LOCATION PROBLEMS. Unpublished memorandum, December, 1963; Roberts, Paul O., and Suhrbier, John H., op.cit.

form Operators, etc.

2. For levels for which well-defined programs or procedures
    do not exist now (such as reconnaissance), consideration
    should be given to the development of such Single-Level
    Operators. To determine relative priorities for these
    operators, prototype location problems would be analyzed.
    These analyses would be similar to the experiments in
    operator characteristics described above. To do this, we
    would establish a set of prototype location problems. The
    essential characteristic of each prototype problem would
    be expressed in terms of a prior. Then, the expected cost
    of the optimal sequence of experiments would be calculated
    (using GUIDE I or a similar program), for different combina-
    tions of operators, and with variations in the operator
    characteristics. The results, averaged over expected prob-
    lem types or analyzed qualitatively, would be useful in
    setting priorities for development of operators with cer-
    tain characteristics. For instance, with the operators
    in the example we used in Chapter III, we might find that
    if the process is unconstrained, operator II is not optimum
    for any prototype prior distribution unless its cost is less
    than that for operator I.

    It is our guess that such an analysis would point up
    a clear need for a variety of higher-level models for route
    location, which are not now available in any formalized,
    reproducible form.[1]

----

[1] That is, there clearly are higher-level models, but these are
pretty much describable only as "engineering judgement."

3. The same kinds of analyses of prototype problems would be useful in designing the basic operational policies of the system. These analyses would be much like the constraint analyses described above, in that the operators would be held fixed, but different operational policies would be explored. For example:

a) constraints similar to those described above: These would reflect alternate organizational structures for the human aspects of the man-machine system. These constraints can also be considered as deliberate strategies: they are deliberate policies adopted for reasons external to our present consideration (administrative reasons, economic use of personnel, e.g.) and the value of these considerations must be weighted against the expected cost incurred, as computed by GUIDE I.

b) basic rules for allocating different types of computer and non-computer storage space to various functions. To illustrate: in a completely unconstrained location process, the engineer may be primarily working at low levels of analysis, alignments and profiles for example. The data for reconnaissance analyses is bulky, and requires large amounts of storage space. Instead of using high-cost, fast access, priority storage for this data (e.g., core or disc files) it can be stored in slower access, less-expensive storage (e.g., magnetic tape or cards) if a computation with GUIDE indicates that the probability of jumping-back to the reconnaissance level is sufficiently low.

c) simple guide rules for deciding the next experiment to perform: if the computation time for active use of GUIDE remains large, it may be desirable to develop simpler rules; these would be tested in prototype problems against the results of GUIDE computations.

4. Current investigations indicate that it may be feasible to construct some fully-automated Single-Level Operators (i.e., requiring no engineer intervention). The present programs, for alignment generation[1] and for profile generation,[2] require the specification of certain parameter values. An appropriate role for GUIDE would be the control of several automated Single-Level Operators, in the sense of determining which to use next at any point, and selecting the parameter settings to be used. The combination of several automated Single-Level Operators and GUIDE in this way would yield a module that could itself be considered as a unitary Single-Level Operator.[3]

5. It is highly desirable to develop techniques for determining the probabilistic characteristics of operators directly. Probably the best approach is the learning scheme outlined in Section 2.9. In this way, the role of GUIDE in the integrated location system would be less sensitive to judgements of relatively poor engineers:

[1]Gladding, Dale, AUTOMATIC SELECTION OF HORIZONTAL ALIGNMENTS FOR HIGHWAY LOCATION. Unpublished M.S. thesis, M.I.T. (1964).

[2]Suhrbier, John H., THE USE OF ELECTRONIC DIGITAL COMPUTERS FOR THE AUTOMATIC SELECTION AND EVALUATION OF HIGHWAY PROFILES. Unpublished M.S. thesis, M.I.T. (1963).

[3]Miller, George A., Eugene Galanter, and Karl H. Pribram, PLANS AND THE STRUCTURE OF BEHAVIOR. New York: Henry Holt and Company (1960).

after a few experiments, the observed performance of
the engineer would reduce the significance of his prior
judgements.

Finally, when we look at the future development of this location system, we see several directions in which additional development of the model of hierarchical structure should go:

1. In the present model of hierarchical structure, locations
    are defined as the full length of road between two termini.
    The model should be extended to allow segmentation of
    routes into links as is often done in the location process.
    For example, doing a lower-level analysis of only a crucial
    segment of a location may give a great deal of information.
    One difficult aspect of this extension is that provision
    must be made for the case where one segment belongs to
    several alternative locations.

2. A second necessary extension is to include stage costs,
    for the cost of operators. For example, before using
    the Digital Terrain Model system, it is necessary to
    invest a sizeable amount of capital for the terrain
    data of the band of interest. However, this cost is
    incurred only once, and is not associated with the band-
    of-interest operator itself (because the band-of-interest
    may be rejected for further analysis, in which case the
    cost of the data will not be incurred). This is a fairly
    simple addition to the present program, and will increase
    its applicability to location problems.

3. The development of GUIDE pinpoints the need for a decision theory capable of moving beyond the assumption of a cardinal utility. (As we pointed out in Section 2.4, GUIDE is based upon this assumption.) Clearly, if we are to extend our location system beyond the relatively simple "rural" location problem (Section 1-1.3), for instance to the problems of urban transportation, we must develop such a decision theory. To use the present formulation of GUIDE, or any other decision procedure with the same assumptions, is unrealistic in such problems.

REFERENCES

Alexander, Christopher, NOTES ON THE SYNTHESIS OF FORM. Cambridge, Massachusetts: Harvard University Press (1964).

Alexander, Christopher, and Marvin L. Manheim, THE DESIGN OF HIGH-WAY INTERCHANGES: AN EXAMPLE OF A GENERAL METHOD FOR ANALYSING ENGINEERING DESIGN PROBLEMS. Research report R62-1, Cambridge, Massachusetts: Civil Engineering Systems Laboratory, M.I.T. (1962).

_____, HIDECS 2: A COMPUTER PROGRAM FOR THE HIERARCHICAL DECOM-POSITION OF A SET WHICH HAS AN ASSOCIATED LINEAR GRAPH. Research report R62-2, Cambridge, Massachusetts: Civil Engineering Sys-tems Laboratory, M.I.T. (1962).

_____, THE USE OF DIAGRAMS IN HIGHWAY ROUTE LOCATION: AN EXPERIMENT. Research report R62-3, Cambridge, Massachusetts: Civil Engineering Systems Laboratory, M.I.T. (1962).

American Association of State Highway Officials, A POLICY ON ARTERIAL HIGHWAYS IN URBAN AREAS. Washington, D.C.: the Association (1957).

_____, A POLICY ON GEOMETRIC DESIGN OF RURAL HIGHWAYS. Washington, D.C.: the Association (1954).

Cohen, John, "Subjective probability," SCIENTIFIC AMERICAN. 197:5 (November 1953), pp. 128-138.

Feigenbaum, Edward A., and Julian Feldman, COMPUTERS AND THOUGHT. New York: McGraw-Hill (1963).

Gladding, Dale, AUTOMATIC SELECTION OF HORIZONTAL ALIGNMENTS FOR HIGHWAY LOCATION. Unpublished M.S. thesis, M.I.T. (1964).

Grant, Eugene L., PRINCIPLES OF ENGINEERING ECONOMY. New York: Ronald Press (1950).

Hildreth, Clifford, "Bayesian statisticians and remote clients," ECONOMETRICA 31:3 (July 1963) pp. 422-438.

Lang, A.S., THE STRUCTURE OF HIGHWAY DESIGN DECISIONS. Unpublished M.S. thesis, M.I.T. (1961).

Lang, A.S., and Martin Wohl, "Evaluation of highway impact," in SOME EVALUATIONS OF HIGHWAY IMPROVEMENT IMPACTS. Bulletin 268, Washingtin, D.C.: Highway Research Board (1960) pp. 105-119.

Luce, R. Duncan, and Howard Raiffa, GAMES AND DECISIONS. New York: John Wiley and Sons (1957).

Manheim, Marvin L., "Data accuracy in route location," TRAFFIC QUARTERLY. January, 1961.

_____, MODEL-BUILDING AND DECISION-MAKING. Research report R62-10, Cambridge, Massachusetts: Civil Engineering Systems Laboratory, M.I.T. (1962).

Martin, Brian V., F. W. Memmott, and A.J. Bone, PRINCIPLES AND TECHNIQUES FOR PREDICTING FUTURE DEMAND FOR URBAN AREA TRANS-PORTATION. Research report R63-1, Cambridge, Massachusetts: Civil Engineering Systems Laboratory, M.I.T. (1963).

M.I.T. Computation Center, THE COMPATIBLE TIME-SHARING SYSTEM: A PROGRAMMER'S GUIDE. Cambridge, Massachusetts: the M.I.T. Press (1963).

Miller, C.L., MAN-MACHINE COMMUNICATIONS IN CIVIL ENGINEERING. Technical paper T63-3, Cambridge, Massachusetts: Department of Civil Engineering, M.I.T. (1963).

Miller, George A., Eugene Galanter, and Karl H. Pribram, PLANS AND THE STRUCTURE OF BEHAVIOR. New York: Henry Holt and Company (1960).

Minsky, Marvin, "Steps toward artificial intelligence," in Feigenbaum and Feldman, COMPUTERS AND THOUGHT (q.v.).

Morris, William T., ENGINEERING ECONOMY. Homewood, Illinois: Richard D. Irwin (1960).

Mood, Alexander M., and Franklin A. Graybill, INTRODUCTION TO THE THEORY OF STATISTICS. New York: McGraw-Hill (1963).

Raiffa, Howard, and Robert Schlaifer, APPLIED STATISTICAL DECI-SION THEORY. Boston: Division of Research, Graduate School of Business Administration, Harvard University (1961).

Rey, Guido, and C.B. Tilanus, "Input-output forecasts for the Netherlands, 1949-1958," ECONOMETRICA, 31:3 (July, 1963) pp. 454-463.

Roberts, Paul O., Marvin L. Manheim, and John H. Suhrbier, A MAN-MACHINE SYSTEM FOR SOLVING HIGHWAY LOCATION PROBLEMS. Unpub-lished memorandum, December, 1963.

Roberts, P.O., and John H. Suhrbier, HIGHWAY LOCATION ANALYSIS: AN EXAMPLE PROBLEM. Research report R62-40, Cambridge, Massachusetts: Civil Engineering Systems Laboratory, M.I.T. (1962).

Roberts, P.O., and A. Villaveces, DTM DESIGN SYSTEM, 20K PROGRAM MANUAL. Research report R62-6, Cambridge, Massachusetts: Civil Engineering Systems Laboratory, M.I.T. (December, 1961).

Samuel, A.L., "Some studies in machine learning using the game of checkers," in Feigenbaum and Feldman, COMPUTERS AND THOUGHT (q.v.).

Savage, Leonard J., "Bayesian statistics," in Robert E. Machol and Paul Gray, eds., RECENT DEVELOPMENTS IN INFORMATION AND DECISION PROCESSES. New York: Macmillan Company (1962) pp. 161-194.

_____, THE FOUNDATIONS OF STATISTICS. New York: John Wiley and Sons (1954).

_____, "Subjective probability and statistical practice," Part I of Savage, L.J. et al, THE FOUNDATIONS OF STATISTICAL INFERENCE: A DISCUSSION. London: Methuen and Company (1962).

Schlaifer, Robert, PROBABILITY AND STATISTICS FOR BUSINESS DECISIONS. New York: McGraw-Hill (1959).

Schoeffer, Sidney, "Toward a general theory of rational action," KYKLOS, VII:3 (1954) pp. 245-271.

Simon, H.A. "Theories of decision-making in economics," AMERICAN ECONOMIC REVIEW XLIX:3 (June, 1959).

Smallwood, Richard D., A DECISION STRUCTURE FOR TEACHING MACHINES. Cambridge, Massachusetts: the M.I.T. Press (1962).

Suhrbier, John H., THE USE OF ELECTRONIC DIGITAL COMPUTERS FOR THE AUTOMATIC SELECTION AND EVALUATION OF HIGHWAY PROFILES. Unpublished M.S. thesis, M.I.T. (1963).

Traffic Research Corporation, unpublished reports on EMPIRIC and POLIMETRIC, two models for use by the Boston Regional Planning Project for predicting land use in the Boston region. (1964).

APPENDIX A.
BRIEF INTRODUCTION TO BAYESIAN DECISION THEORY

A.1.   Introduction [1]

The basic elements of the Bayesian Decision Theory (BDT) approach are: the set of terminal actions, A; the set of possible experiments, E; the set of experimental outcomes Z; the states θ; the utility $u(e,z,a,\theta)$; and the probability distributions $P(\theta)$ and $P(z|e,\theta)$.

The basic objective of the decision maker (DM) is to pick some terminal action, a, which will maximise his utility. This is difficult because the utility corresponding to a depends upon the value of the state variable θ. Given the probability distribution over θ, $P(\theta)$, the DM should use the expected-value principle: that is, he should pick that terminal act a for which the expected value of utility, under the distribution $P(\theta)$, is greatest.

When $P(\theta)$ represents the DM's judgement about the relative likelihood of values of θ, we call it a subjective probability. Instead of picking an action a immediately, the engineer does have the option of selecting one or more experiments to be per- formed, in order to get more information about the value of θ. When he performs an experiment e and observes a particular result z, the DM's judgement changes, and there is a corresponding change in the distribution $P(\theta)$.

The prior distribution, denoted as $P'(\theta)$, represents the DM's judgement before performing the experiment; the posterior

---

[1] Raiffa, Howard, and Robert Schlaifer, APPLIED STATISTICAL DECI- SION THEORY. Boston: Graduate School of Business Administration, Harvard University (1961). Discussion in Sections A.1-A.5 follows Chapter I.

distribution, $P''(\theta|z,e)$, expresses his judgement after the experiment e has been performed and the result z observed. The Bayesian assumption is that each experiment e can be characterized by a conditional probability distribution $P(z|\theta,e)$, such that the relationship between the prior and the posterior distributions is given by Bayes Theorem:

$$P''(\theta|z,e) = \frac{P'(\theta)\ P(z|\theta,e)}{\sum_{\theta} P'(\theta)\ p(z|\theta,e).}$$

The objective of the BDT approach is to aid the DM to make a "rational" decision by explicitly considering all possible sequences of experiments, their outcomes, terminal actions, and states. Each such combination has a utility, $u(e,z,a,\theta)$. To find the best sequence, the expected value of the utility of each combination must be computed. This requires a probability distribution; the subjective probability distributions over θ provide this. In order to predict the subjective distributions representing judgements in the future, consequent upon the execution of several experiments and the observations of their results, Bayes Theorem is used. These future distributions could be estimated directly, a priori, conditional upon the specified sequences of experiments and outcomes, but the use of Bayes Theorem is more economical: instead of estimating a variety of possible posteriors, the engineer need only estimate an appropriate conditional for each experiment.

In conclusion: the use of BDT is characterized by the use of subjective probabilities, the use of Bayes Theorem to predict future subjective probabilities, and the computation of expected utility over a large number of sequences of experiments, outcomes, actions, and states.

A.2 Basic data

It is assumed that the following basic data are specified by
the decision-maker (DM):

a) Set of alternative actions. The task of the DM is to
select one action from some set A = (a).

b) State space. The DM believes that his choice of an action
from A is dependent upon the actual value of some variable,
but he does not know with certainty what is the value of
that variable. Such a "state" variable is devoted by θ
(θ may be a vector).

c) Set of experiments: There is available to the DM a set
of experiments E = (e), one of which the DM may elect to
perform in order to get more information about the likelihood of different values of the state variable.

d) Sample space: For every experiment e, there is a space
of possible outcomes of that experiment. By convention,
the space of outcomes Z = (z) is defined as "rich enough
to encompass any outcome of any e in E."[1]

e) Utility evaluation: In a typical sequence of operations,
the DM performs an experiment e, observes a result z,
elects a particular action a, and then discovers that a
particular state θ obtains. The space of all possible

---

[1] Raiffa and Schlaifer, op.cit., p.3.

187

combinations of (e,z,a,θ) is $E \times Z \times A \times \theta$. We assume
that the DM has a single-valued utility function defined
over this space, denoted as $u(e,z,a,\theta)$. That is, the
DM is able to give a numerical score (such as cost in
dollars) to each possible combination of an experiment,
an outcome, an action, and a state of the world. As a
simple example, the utility function may consist of the
sum of the cost of performing the experiment and the
cost associated with the action.

f) <u>Probability assessment.</u> For every possible experiment
e which might be performed, the DM is able to specify
a joint probability measure $P(\theta,z|e)$ over the space
$\theta \times Z$. From this measure, these four others can be
computed:
  i) the marginal measure $P'(\theta)$, the probability of
      different states θ.[1]
  ii) the conditional measure $P(z|e,\theta)$, the probability
      that the outcome z will be observed if the experi-
      ment e is performed and θ is the value of the
      state variable.
  iii) the marginal measure $P(z|e)$, the probability of
      getting outcome z from experiment e, when the
      state θ is not specified.
  iv) the conditional measure $P''(\theta|z,e)$, the likelihood
      of different states θ, given z and e.

A.3 Interpreting the probability measures

There are three ways $P(\theta,z|e)$ may be specified:

---

[1] Note that the DM's prior is assumed independent of the experi-
ment to be performed: i.e., $P'(\theta) = P'(\theta|e_i)$, for all e_i.

188

i)   direct estimation of $P(\theta, z|e)$.

ii)   estimation of $P'(\theta)$ and $P(z|\theta, e)$, then computing the other two distributions (iii and iv, above).

iii)   estimation of $P(z|e)$ and $P''(\theta|z, e)$, then computing the joint distribution and the other two distributions (i and ii, above).

The usual approach is that outlined in (ii). However, in some applications, as Raiffa and Schlaifer point out,[1] the formulation (iii) may be more appropriate. Since the necessary functions are specified completely by any of the three approaches, the operations for computing the optimal decision are identical. We actually use both approaches: the DM estimates $P(z|e)$, and $P''(\theta|z, e)$; but the computer program translates, computes, and operates with $P'(\theta)$ and $P(z|\theta, e)$. (See Section II-3.5.)

The measure $P'(\theta)$ is termed a prior probability over the unknown state variables. "It is the measure which the decision-maker assigns or would assign to θ prior to knowing the outcome z of the experiment e."[2]

$P'(\theta)$ is estimated by the DM, and expresses his judgements about the relative likelihoods of the different values of θ. The prior probability can be thought of as a convenient weighting function, which follows the conventions sufficiently to operate in all relevant respects like a probability function.[3]

----

[1] op.cit., p.5, 22, pp.58-69

[2] op.cit., p.4

[3] For a detailed development of subjective probability from basic postulates, see Leonard J. Savage, THE FOUNDATIONS OF STATISTICS. New York: John Wiley & Sons. (1954).

P'(θ) is an expression of the DM's judgement <u>before</u> he
executes an experiment; after he executes some experiment e
and observes the result z, his judgement about the relative
likelihood of different states θ will, in general, be different.
Denote the distribution which presents this revised judgement
as F(θ|z,e).

The distribution F(θ|z,e) could be obtained in either of
two ways:
i)   it can be estimated directly, in the same way as the
      prior P'(θ) was itself estimated;
ii)   it can be computed, by assuming that the DM is willing
      to act as if P(θ|z,e) = P''(θ|z,e), where P''(θ|z,e) is
      related to the prior P'(θ) by Bayes Theorem,

$$P''(\theta|z,e) = \frac{P'(\theta)\ P(z|\theta,e)}{\sum_{\theta} P'(\theta)\ P(z|\theta,e)}$$

The basic assumption of the Bayesian point of view is that the
DM is willing to act as if both methods for obtaining F will
yield the same results.

A.4 Representation: the decision tree

The basic data of the decision problem can be represented
by a "decision tree," as illustrated in Figure A-1. (The example
shown will be described in detail below.)

The first task of the DM is to choose an experiment (we allow
the option of the "null," or do-nothing, experiment). This is
illustrated by a set of branches, one each corresponding to different possible experiments. Having performed an experiment,

the DM next observes the outcome of that experiment; therefore, for every branch corresponding to an experiment, there is a set of branches corresponding to each possible outcome of that experiment. When the outcome is observed, the DM must then choose an action. The choices are indicated, after each outcome branch. Finally, having performed an experiment, observed its outcome, and chosen an action, the DM receives a reward, represented by the utility function, which depends upon the actual state of nature. Therefore, for each action branch, there is a set of branches corresponding to each possible state of the world.

Any sequence of (experiment, outcome, action, state) can be represented by a path through this tree. The final point corresponds to the end of the cycle; for that point there is a value, the utility $u(e,z,a,\theta)$. The desirability of that sequence (e,z,a,θ) is completely summarized by the value of the utility, $u(e,z,a,\theta)$.

A.5 Operating upon the data to specify a decision

After performing an experiment and observing the result, the probability over the state, θ, is given by $P''(\theta|z,e)$. At this point, the DM can choose among the acts, A. For each such act, the expected utility can be computed as

$$u^{*}(a,e,z) = \sum_{\theta} u(e,z,a,\theta) \cdot P''(\theta|z,e).$$

Consistent with the assumptions of which the Bayesian point of view consists,[1] we assume that the DM is rational, in the sense that he will choose that action a for which $u^{*}(a,e,z)$ is

[1] Savage, op.cit.

is greatest. Therefore, we define $u^*(e,z) = \max\limits_{a} u^*(a,e,z)$
This is the expected utility of performing experiment e and
observing the result z.

For any experiment e, the probability of observing a result
z is the marginal probability $P(z|e)$. With the utility of each
outcome, $u^*(e,z)$, known, the expected utility for each experi-
ment can be computed as $u^*(e) = \sum\limits_{z} u^*(e,z)\, P(z|e)$. Consistent
with the above-mentioned assumptions, we again postulate that
the DM will choose that experiment e for which the expected
utility $u^*(e)$ is maximum. We call this u^*, the utility of the
optimal action for the DM, under the given probability distributions: $u^* = \max\limits_{e} u^*(e)$.

In order to solve his decision problem, the DM will first
choose that experiment e for which the expected return, as
represented by $u^*(e)$, is the greatest. Then, having performed
that experiment and observed the result z, he will have a poste-
rior probability $P''(\theta|z,e)$, and he will choose that action, a,
for which $u^*(a,z,e)$ is greatest.

A.6 The null experiment

There generally is the option of performing no experiment
at all, but choosing an action, a, immediately. In this case,
the relevant probability distribution is $P'(\theta)$, and the action
which the DM should select (consistent with the assumptions) is
that a for which $u^*(a)$ is maximum. In this case,

$$u^*(a) = \sum\limits_{\theta} u(a,\theta) \cdot P'(\theta).$$

We will include this case of the "null" experiment in our

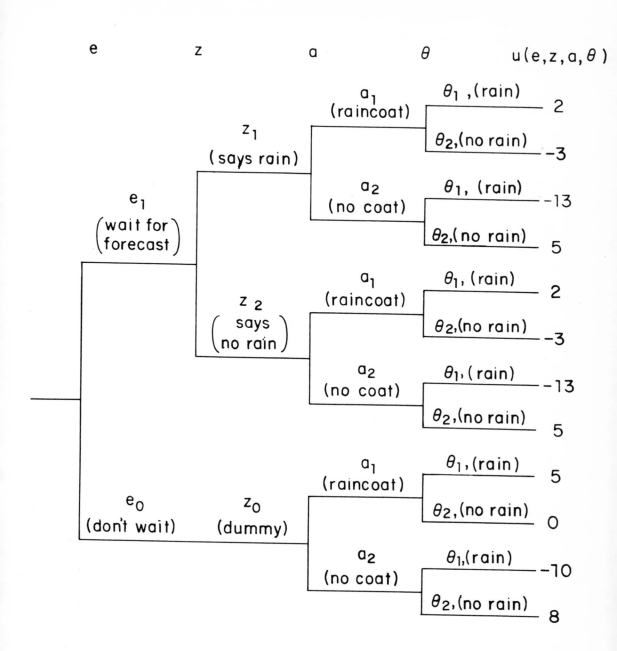

FIGURE A-1 DECISION TREE FOR THE WEATHER PROBLEM

previous treatment by defining an experiment e_o which corresponds
to not performing any experiment at all. The corresponding outcomes z are all dummies, and the conditional probability
$P''(\theta|e_o,z) = P'(\theta)$. In this way, the computations outlined in
the previous section are made completely general, comprehending
the null experiment as well.

A.7 Resume: the sequence of operations

To summarize, we list in step-wise sequence the operations
required in making a decision according to the postulated system.
1. List all possible actions, a.
2. List all possible states of the world, θ.
3. List the possible experiments e, including the null, e_o.
4. For each experiment, list all possible outcomes z.

These first four steps are equivalent to constructing
the decision tree.

5. Determine for each combination of (experiment, outcome,
action, state) its relative desirability - i.e.,
$u(e,z,a,\theta)$. (This is equivalent to placing a numerical
utility at the tip of each path through the decision
tree.)
6. Express the DM's prior judgement about the relative likelihood of different states θ in the form of a probability
distribution $P'(\theta)$. "Prior" indicates that this is prior
to performing any experiment.
7. For each experiment, determine its probability character-
istic, as given by $P(z|\theta,e)$. Steps 6 and 7 generate the
joint probability distribution $P(\theta,z|e)$. They can be
replaced by any other operations which produce the same

194

result, the joint probability distribution $P(\theta, z|e)$;
the marginal, $P'(\theta)$; and the conditional $P(z|\theta, e)$.

8. For each (experiment, outcome) combination, compute
   the posterior distribution $P''(\theta|z, e)$, by Bayes Theorem.

$$P''(\theta|z,e) = \frac{P'(\theta) \cdot P(z|\theta,e)}{\sum_{\theta} P'(\theta)\, P(z|\theta,e)}$$

9. Determine the expected utility for each act a, for
   each (experiment, outcome) combination, by
   $u^{*}(a,z,e) = \sum_{\theta} P''(\theta|z,e) \cdot u(e,z,a,\theta)$.

10. For each (experiment, outcome) combination, determine
    the optimal act and its associated utility,
    $u^{*}(z,e) = \max_{a} u^{*}(a,z,e)$.

11. For each experiment, compute the probability of each
    particular outcome z, given by the marginal distribu-
    tion $P(z|e)$.

12. For each experiment, determine the expected return $u^{*}(e)$,
    by $u^{*}(e) = \sum_{z} P(z|e) \cdot u^{*}(z,e)$.

13. The optimal experiment e^{*} is that e for which $u^{*}(e)$ is a
    maximum. Since the null experiment is also considered,
    the optimal experiment may turn out to be "no experiment,"
    indicating that an action should be selected without
    experimentation.

$$u^{*}(e^{*}) = \max_{e} u^{*}(e) \; .$$

A.8 Illustration of the computational procedures: the weather game

On a partly-cloudy Monday morning, the engineer stands at his
window, about to rush out the door: should he take his raincoat or
not? It looks like rain, and if it rains and he hasn't got his

raincoat with him, getting soaked can be awfully uncomfortable.
On the other hand, carrying the raincoat over his shoulder, or
wearing it, is also uncomfortable, if it doesn't rain and the
temperature remains at 80°. Of course, there is always the
possibility of waiting for the eight o'clock weather forecast,
but that means he'd be late, and that's embarassing; besides,
he doesn't have complete confidence in the weather bureau's forecast. In fact, the probability that the weather bureau gives the
right answer is only .7, or so our engineer believes. Furthermore, on the basis of his scowling examination of the scurrying
clouds out his window, the engineer feels that the chances of
rain are about .4.

In the time it takes a towering grey monster to move from
the left edge of the window to the center, our hero has formulated his problem in a Bayesian decision theory framework:

1. List actions:

a_1 = take raincoat

a_2 = leave it at home

2. List states:

θ_1 = it rains

θ_2 = it doesn't

3. List experiments:

e_1 = wait for the weather forecast

e_o = don't wait for the forecast

4. List outcomes:

z_1 = weather forecast says rain

z_2 = weather forecast says no rain

z_o = dummy outcome of the null experiment

5. Utility: he decides his utilities can be decomposed
into two parts, one depending only upon the experiment he picks, and the other only on the rain-raincoat

pair: $u(e,z,a,\theta) = u(e,z) + u(a,\theta)$

$u(a,\theta)$:	θ_1	θ_2
a_1	5	0
a_2	-10	8

$u(e,z)$:	e_o	e_1
	0	-3

6. Formulate the prior:

$P'(\theta_1) = 0.4$

$P'(\theta_2) = 0.6$

7. Determine the probability characteristic for each experiment:

$$P(z_1|\theta_1,e_1) = .7^1$$
$$P(z_2|\theta_1,e_1) = .3$$
$$P(z_1|\theta_2,e_1) = .3$$
$$P(z_2|\theta_2,e_1) = .7$$
$$P(z_o|\theta_1,e_o) = 1.0$$
$$P(z_o|\theta_2,e_o) = 1.0$$

The decision tree is sketched in Figure A-1.

Since our highly-rational engineer has had the foresight to install a time-sharing console in his living room, and to write an appropriate program for such occasions as this, it is a matter of seconds for him to have the following computations executed:

---

[1] The verbal statement, "the probability that the weather bureau gives the right answer is .7," can be interpreted two ways:

a) $P(z_1|\theta_1,e_1) = .7 =$ the probability that the weather bureau says rain, given that it will rain;

b) $P(\theta_1|z_1,e_1) = .7 =$ the probability that it will rain, given that the weather bureau forecasts rain.

Either formulation is consistent with the verbal statement, indicating the looseness of that statement. We will use (a).

8. Calculate posterior distributions:

$$P''(\theta_1 | z_0, e_0) = P'(\theta_1) = .4$$

$$P''(\theta_2 | z_0, e_0) = P'(\theta_2) = .6$$

$$P''(\theta_1 | z_1, e_1) = \frac{P'(\theta_1)\ P(z_1 | \theta_1, e_1)}{P'(\theta_1)\ P(z_1 | \theta_1, e_1) + P'(\theta_2)\ P(z_1 | \theta_2, e_1)}$$

$$= \frac{(.4) \times (.7)}{(.4)\ (.7) + (.6)\ (.3)} = .61$$

$$P''(\theta_2 | z_1, e_1) = \frac{(.6)\ (.3)}{(.4)\ (.7) + (.6)\ (.3)} = .39$$

$$P''(\theta_1 | z_2, e_1) = \frac{P'(\theta_1)\ P(z_2 | \theta_1, e_1)}{P'(\theta_1)\ P(z_2 | \theta_1, e_1) + P'(\theta_2)\ P(z_2 | \theta_2, e_1)}$$

$$= \frac{(.4)\ (.3)}{(.4)\ (.3) + (.6)\ (.7)} = .22$$

$$P''(\theta_2 | z_2, e_2) = \frac{(.6)\ (.7)}{(.4)\ (.3) + (.6)\ (.7)} = .78$$

9. Calculate $u^*(a,z,e)$:

$$u^*(a_1,z_0,e_0) = P''(\theta_1|z_0,e_0)\, u(e_0,z_0,a_1,\theta_1) + P''(\theta_2|z_0,e_0) \cdot$$

$$u(e_0,z_0,a_1,\theta_2)$$

$$= (.4)\ (0 + 5) + (.6)\ (0 + 0)$$

$$= 2.0$$

$$u^*(a_2,z_0,e_0) = P''(\theta_1|z_0,e_0) \cdot u(e_0,z_0,a_2,\theta_1) + P''(\theta_2|z_0,e_0) \cdot$$

$$u(e_0,z_0,a_2,\theta_2)$$

$$= (.4)\ (0-10) + (.6)\ (0 + 8)$$

$$= 0.8$$

$$u^*(a_1,z_1,e_1) = P''(\theta_1|z_1,e_1) \cdot u(e_1,z_1,a_1,\theta_1) + P''(\theta_2|z_1,e_1) \cdot$$

$$u(e_1,z_1,a_1,\theta_2)$$

$$= (.61)\ (5-3) + (.39)\ (0-3) = 0.05$$

$$u^*(a_2,z_1,e_1) = -5.98$$

$$u^*(a_1,z_2,e_1) = -1.90$$

$$u^*(a_2,z_2,e_1) = +1.04$$

10. For each (e,z) combination, determine the optimal act a^* and its associated utility:

(e_o,z_o):
$$u^*(a_1,z_o,e_o) = 2$$
$$u^*(a_2,z_o,e_o) = 0.8$$
$$u^*(e_o,z_o) = \max_a \ u^*(a,z,e) = 2$$

$$a^*(e_o,z_o) = a_1$$

(e_1,z_1):
$$u^*(a_1,z_1,e_1) = + 0.05$$
$$u^*(a_2,z_1,e_1) = - 5.98$$
$$u^*(e_1,z_1) = + 0.05$$

$$a^*(e_1,z_1) = a_1$$

(e_1,z_2):
$$u^*(a_1,z_2,e_1) = - 1.90$$
$$u^*(a_2,z_2,e_1) = + 1.04$$
$$u^*(e_1,z_2) = + 1.04$$

$$a^*(e_1,z_2) = a_2$$

11. Compute the marginal $P(z|e)$:

$$P(z_1|e_1)=P'(\theta_1) \cdot P(z_1|e_1,\theta_1) + P(\theta_2) \cdot P(z_1|e_1,\theta_2)$$

$$= (.4)\ (.7) + (.6)\ (.3) = .46$$

$$P(z_2|e_1)= P'(\theta_1) \cdot P(z_2|e_1,\theta_1) + P'(\theta_2) \cdot P(z_2|e_1,\theta_2)$$

$$= (.4) \cdot (.3) + (.6)\ (.7) = .54$$

$$P(z_o|e_o)= 1$$

12. Calculate $u^*(e)$:

$$u^*(e_1) = P(z_1|e_1) \cdot u^*(e_1, z_1) + P(z_2|e_1) \cdot u^*(e_1, z_2)$$

$$= (.46) \; (+ 0.05) + (.54) \; (+ 1.04) = .58$$

$$u^*(e_0) = P(z_0|e_0) \cdot u^*(e_0, z_0) = u^*(e_0, z_0) = 2$$

13. Find e^*, the optimal experiment:

$$u^*(e^*) = \max_e u^*(e) = \max u^*(e_0) \cdot u^*(e_1) = 2; \quad e^* = e_0.$$

Conclusion: as a result of his computations, the engineer concludes that he should not wait for the weather forecast.

APPENDIX B.

FLOW CHARTS FOR GUIDE I

LIST OF FLOW CHARTS

Control routines:

1. MAIN

2. CNTRL

Other subprograms:

3. ANDREA

4. BAYES(JOLD,JNEW)

5. EVAL

6. INPUT

7. INPUTB

8. JUGGLE

9. PERMIS(XPER)

10. PLOT

11. RESULT

12. SLOSH

13. STOP

14. TAPLAY

15. UPDATE

FAP subprograms not shown:

16. RENAME

17. SETX

Notes:

1. Except where indicated otherwise in these flow charts the
   term "level" has exactly the opposite meaning to that in
   the text: the level of an action here is the same as the
   number of the Single-Level Operator which produced that
   action. The program variable LEVEL(KK,JJ) has this same
   meaning. For example, if there are three operators, the
   universal action has level 0, while elemental actions are
   at level 3. For comparison, cf. Section II-2.3.

2. We use two symbols for the cost of the cheapest elemental
   action found so far at any position in the location process:
   RALT, and R.

MAIN PROGRAM

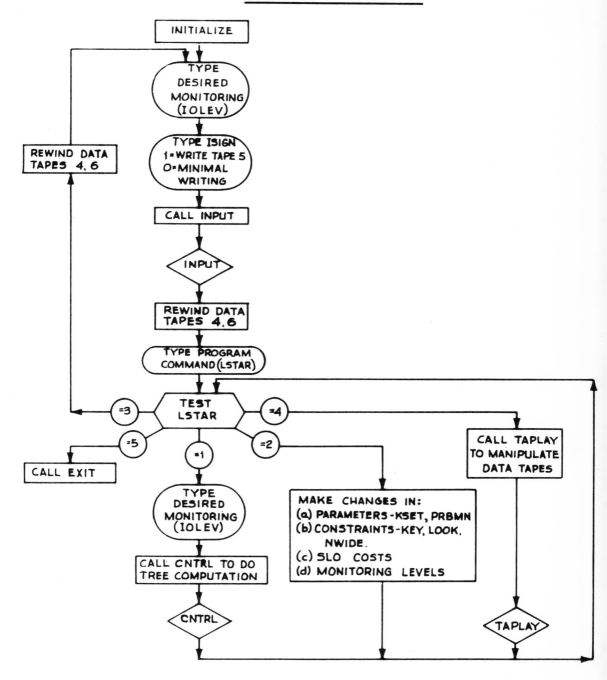

SUBROUTINE CNTRL

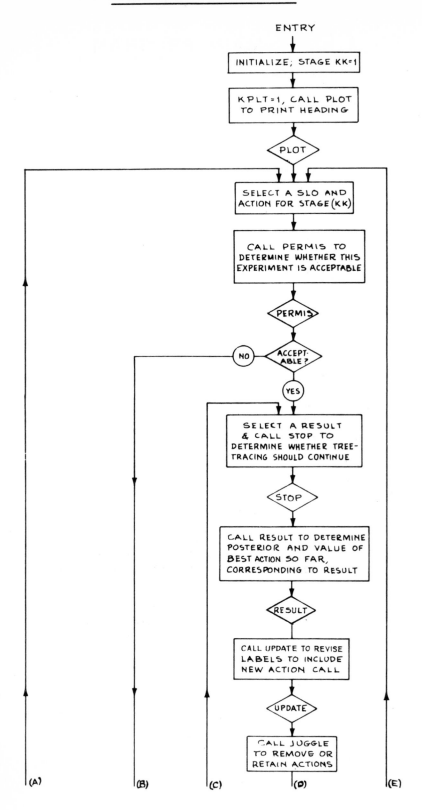

ENTRY

INITIALIZE; STAGE KK=1

KPLT=1, CALL PLOT TO PRINT HEADING

PLOT

SELECT A SLO AND ACTION FOR STAGE(KK)

CALL PERMIS TO DETERMINE WHETHER THIS EXPERIMENT IS ACCEPTABLE

PERMIS

NO

ACCEPT-ABLE ?

YES

SELECT A RESULT & CALL STOP TO DETERMINE WHETHER TREE-TRACING SHOULD CONTINUE

STOP

CALL RESULT TO DETERMINE POSTERIOR AND VALUE OF BEST ACTION SO FAR, CORRESPONDING TO RESULT

RESULT

CALL UPDATE TO REVISE LABELS TO INCLUDE NEW ACTION CALL

UPDATE

CALL JUGGLE TO REMOVE OR RETAIN ACTIONS

(A)   (B)   (C)   (D)   (E)

SUBROUTINE CNTRL (CONT'D)

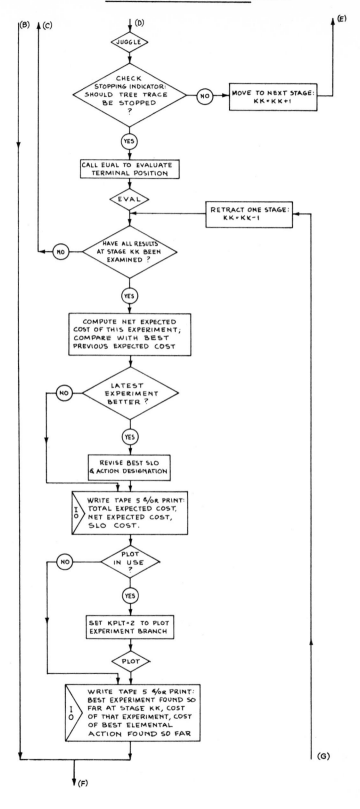

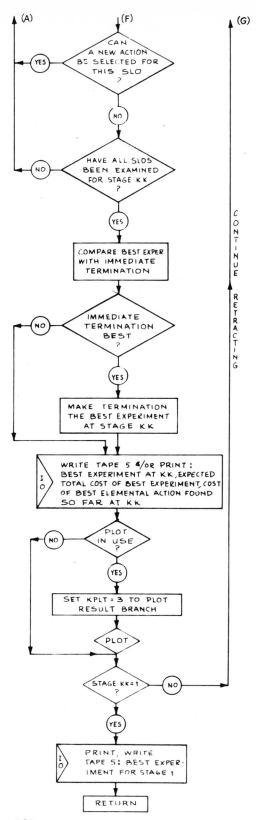

SUBROUTINE ANDREA

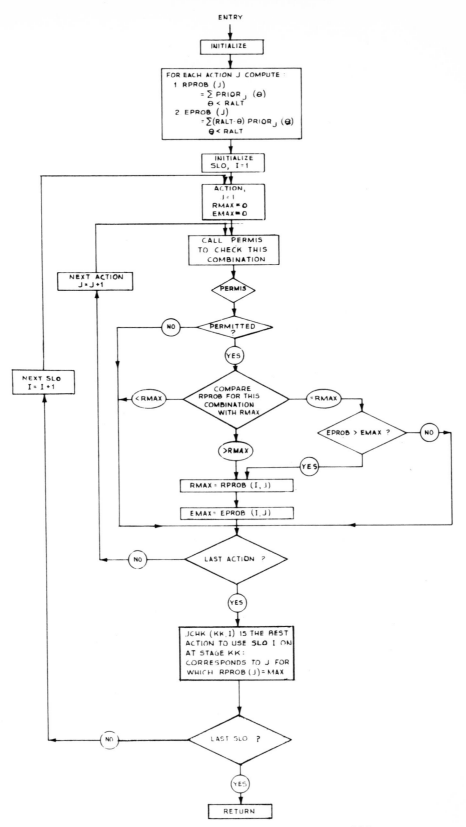

ENTRY

INITIALIZE

FOR EACH ACTION J COMPUTE :
1 RPROB (J)
$= \sum_{\theta < RALT} PRIOR_J (\theta)$
2 EPROB (J)
$= \sum_{\theta < RALT} (RALT-\theta) PRIOR_J (\theta)$

INITIALIZE
SLO, I =1

ACTION,
I = 1
RMAX = 0
EMAX = 0

CALL PERMIS
TO CHECK THIS
COMBINATION

PERMIS

NEXT ACTION
J = J+1

PERMITTED
?

NO

YES

NEXT SLO
I = I + 1

COMPARE
RPROB FOR THIS
COMBINATION
WITH RMAX

< RMAX

= RMAX

EPROB > EMAX ?

NO

> RMAX

YES

RMAX = RPROB (I, J)

EMAX = EPROB (I, J)

LAST ACTION ?

NO

YES

JCHK (KK, I) IS THE BEST
ACTION TO USE SLO I ON
AT STAGE KK:
CORRESPONDS TO J FOR
WHICH RPROB (J) = MAX

LAST SLO ?

NO

YES

RETURN

SUBROUTINE BAYES (JOLD, JNEW)

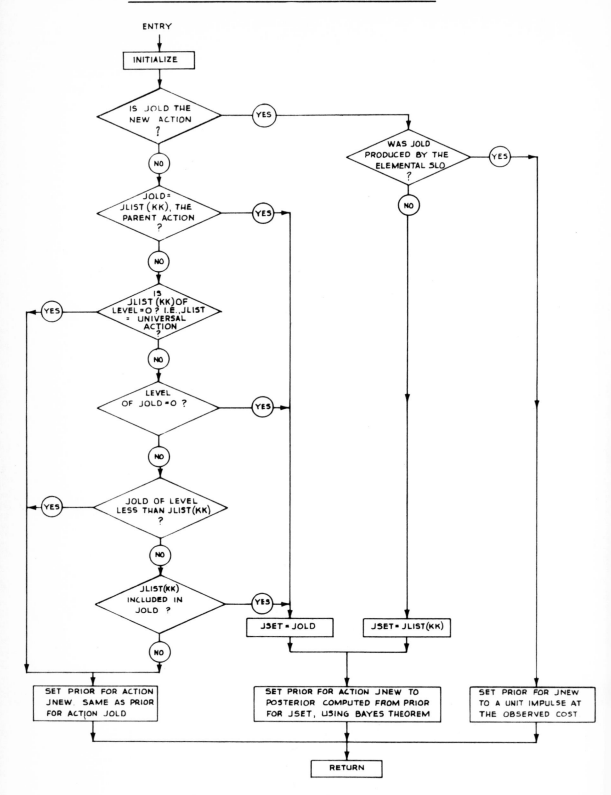

SUBROUTINE EVAL

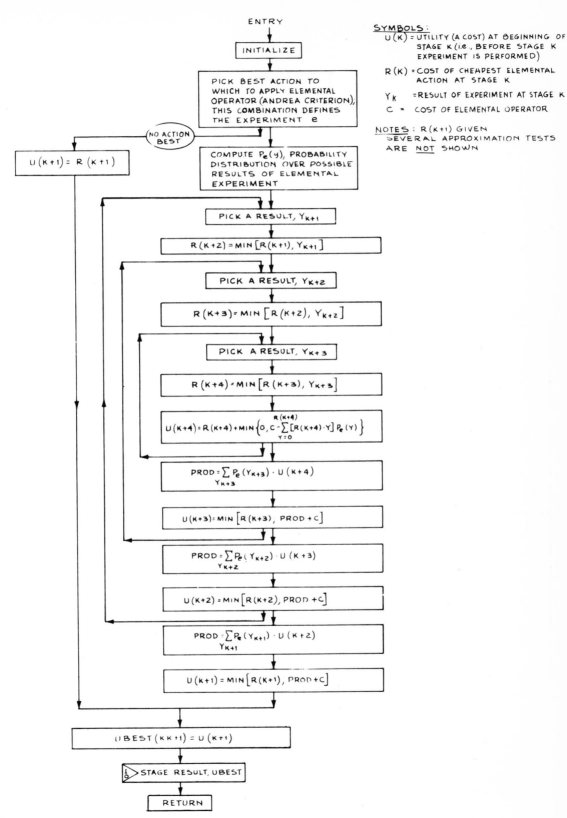

ENTRY

INITIALIZE

PICK BEST ACTION TO WHICH TO APPLY ELEMENTAL OPERATOR (ANDREA CRITERION), THIS COMBINATION DEFINES THE EXPERIMENT e

NO ACTION BEST

$U(K+1) = R(K+1)$

COMPUTE $P_e(y)$, PROBABILITY DISTRIBUTION OVER POSSIBLE RESULTS OF ELEMENTAL EXPERIMENT

PICK A RESULT, Y_{K+1}

$R(K+2) = MIN[R(K+1), Y_{K+1}]$

PICK A RESULT, Y_{K+2}

$R(K+3) = MIN[R(K+2), Y_{K+2}]$

PICK A RESULT, Y_{K+3}

$R(K+4) = MIN[R(K+3), Y_{K+3}]$

$U(K+4) = R(K+4) + MIN\left\{0, C - \sum_{Y=0}^{R(K+4)}[R(K+4) - Y] P_e(Y)\right\}$

$PROD = \sum_{Y_{K+3}} P_e(Y_{K+3}) \cdot U(K+4)$

$U(K+3) = MIN[R(K+3), PROD + C]$

$PROD = \sum_{Y_{K+2}} P_e(Y_{K+2}) \cdot U(K+3)$

$U(K+2) = MIN[R(K+2), PROD + C]$

$PROD = \sum_{Y_{K+1}} P_e(Y_{K+1}) \cdot U(K+2)$

$U(K+1) = MIN[R(K+1), PROD + C]$

$UBEST(KK+1) = U(K+1)$

STAGE RESULT, UBEST

RETURN

SYMBOLS:
$U(K)$ = UTILITY (A COST) AT BEGINNING OF STAGE K (i.e., BEFORE STAGE K EXPERIMENT IS PERFORMED)

$R(K)$ = COST OF CHEAPEST ELEMENTAL ACTION AT STAGE K

Y_K = RESULT OF EXPERIMENT AT STAGE K

C = COST OF ELEMENTAL OPERATOR

NOTES: $R(K+1)$ GIVEN
SEVERAL APPROXIMATION TESTS ARE NOT SHOWN

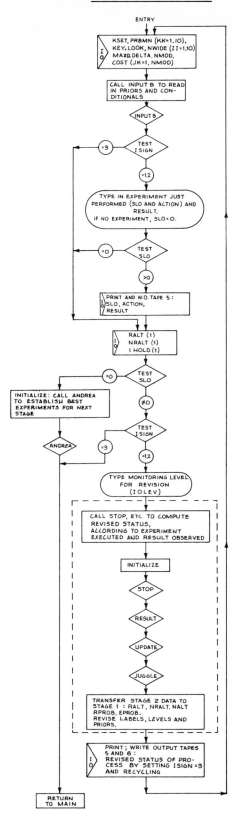

SUBROUTINE INPUT B

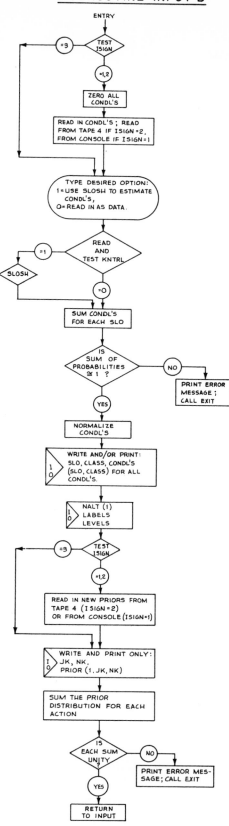

SUBROUTINE JUGGLE

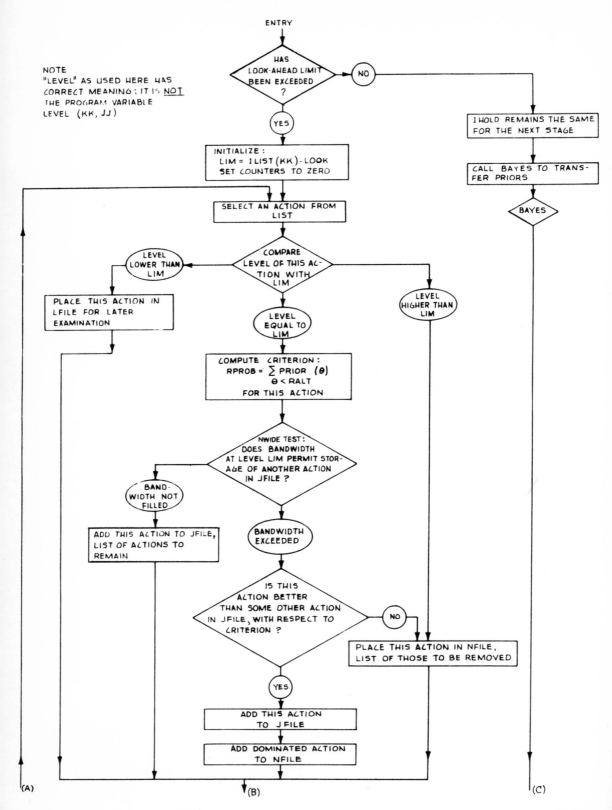

ENTRY

NOTE
"LEVEL" AS USED HERE HAS CORRECT MEANING; IT IS NOT THE PROGRAM VARIABLE LEVEL (KK, JJ)

HAS LOOK-AHEAD LIMIT BEEN EXCEEDED ? — NO

YES

I HOLD REMAINS THE SAME FOR THE NEXT STAGE

CALL BAYES TO TRANSFER PRIORS.

BAYES

INITIALIZE:
LIM = ILIST(KK)-LOOK
SET COUNTERS TO ZERO

SELECT AN ACTION FROM LIST

COMPARE LEVEL OF THIS ACTION WITH LIM

LEVEL LOWER THAN LIM

LEVEL HIGHER THAN LIM

PLACE THIS ACTION IN LFILE FOR LATER EXAMINATION

LEVEL EQUAL TO LIM

COMPUTE CRITERION:
$RPROB = \sum_{\theta < RALT} PRIOR(\theta)$
FOR THIS ACTION

NWIDE TEST:
DOES BANDWIDTH AT LEVEL LIM PERMIT STORAGE OF ANOTHER ACTION IN JFILE ?

BAND-WIDTH NOT FILLED

ADD THIS ACTION TO JFILE, LIST OF ACTIONS TO REMAIN

BANDWIDTH EXCEEDED

IS THIS ACTION BETTER THAN SOME OTHER ACTION IN JFILE, WITH RESPECT TO CRITERION ? — NO

PLACE THIS ACTION IN NFILE, LIST OF THOSE TO BE REMOVED

YES

ADD THIS ACTION TO JFILE

ADD DOMINATED ACTION TO NFILE

(A)

(B)

(C)

216

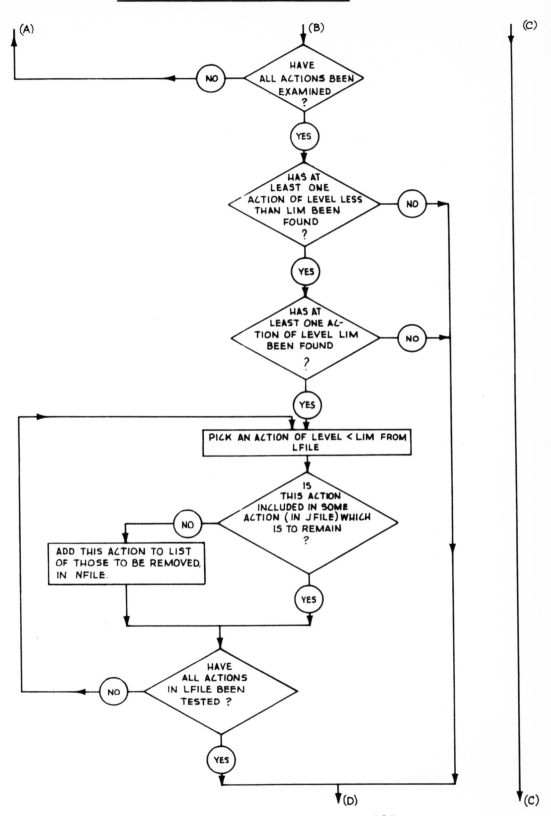

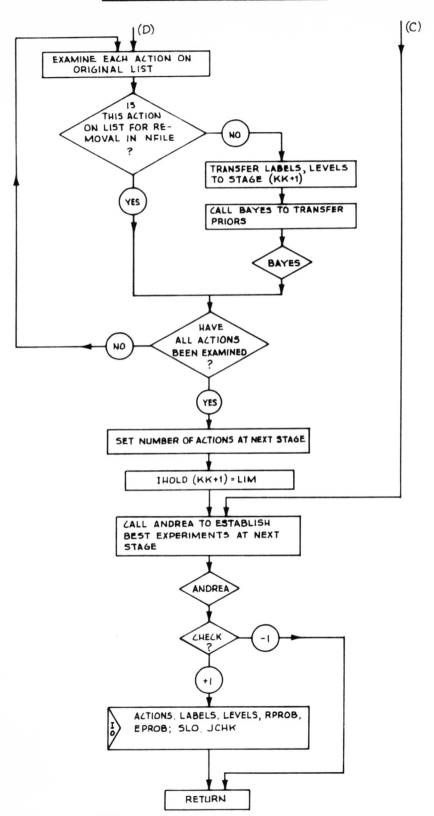

SUBROUTINE PERMIS (XPER)

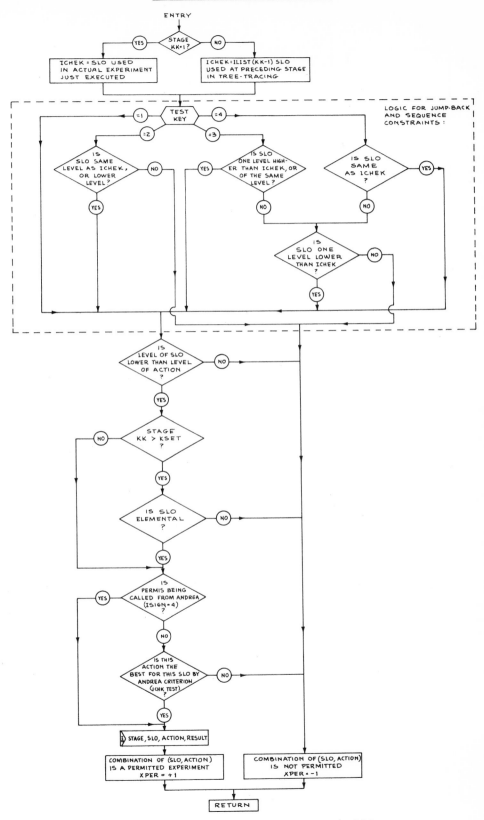

SUBROUTINE PLOT

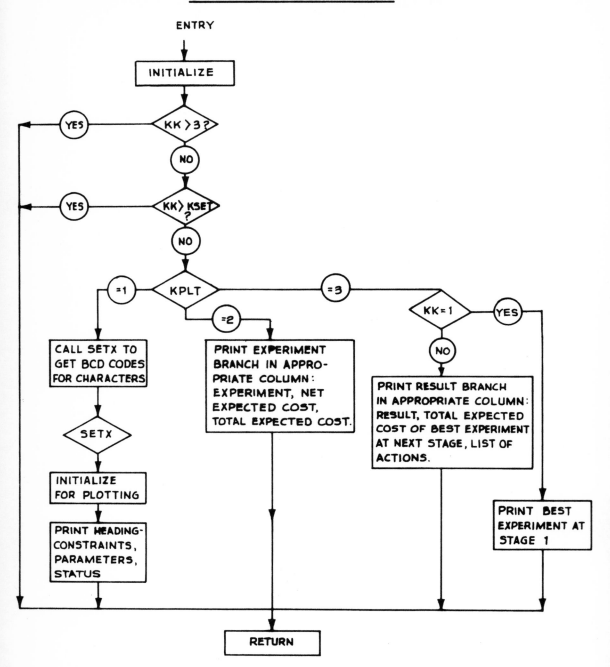

SUBROUTINE RESULT

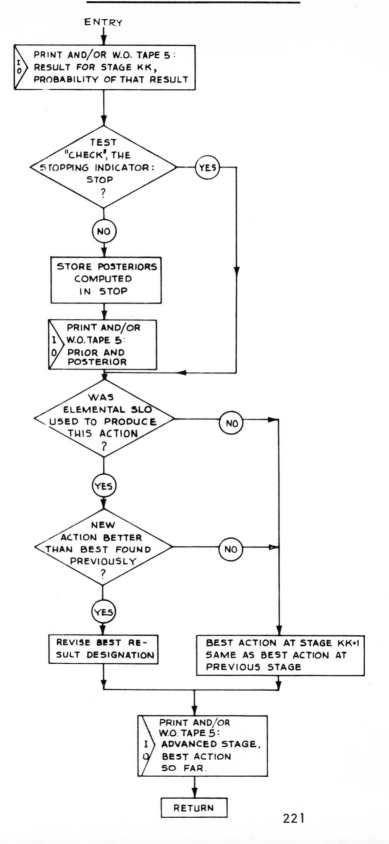

ENTRY

PRINT AND/OR W.O. TAPE 5: RESULT FOR STAGE KK, PROBABILITY OF THAT RESULT
(I / 0)

TEST "CHECK", THE STOPPING INDICATOR: STOP ?
YES
NO

STORE POSTERIORS COMPUTED IN STOP

PRINT AND/OR W.O. TAPE 5: PRIOR AND POSTERIOR
(I / 0)

WAS ELEMENTAL SLO USED TO PRODUCE THIS ACTION ?
NO
YES

NEW ACTION BETTER THAN BEST FOUND PREVIOUSLY ?
NO
YES

REVISE BEST RE-SULT DESIGNATION

BEST ACTION AT STAGE KK+1 SAME AS BEST ACTION AT PREVIOUS STAGE

PRINT AND/OR W.O. TAPE 5: ADVANCED STAGE, BEST ACTION SO FAR.
(I / 0)

RETURN

221

SUBROUTINE SLOSH

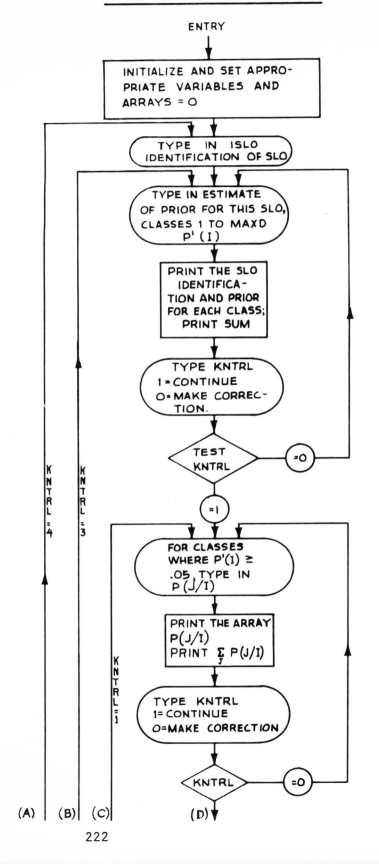

ENTRY

INITIALIZE AND SET APPRO-
PRIATE VARIABLES AND
ARRAYS = O

TYPE IN ISLO
IDENTIFICATION OF SLO

TYPE IN ESTIMATE
OF PRIOR FOR THIS SLO,
CLASSES 1 TO MAXD
P'(I)

PRINT THE SLO
IDENTIFICA-
TION AND PRIOR
FOR EACH CLASS;
PRINT SUM

TYPE KNTRL
1 = CONTINUE
O = MAKE CORREC-
TION.

TEST
KNTRL   =O

=I

FOR CLASSES
WHERE P'(I) ≥
.05 TYPE IN
P(J/I)

PRINT THE ARRAY
P(J/I)
PRINT $\sum_J$ P(J/I)

TYPE KNTRL
1 = CONTINUE
O = MAKE CORRECTION

KNTRL   =O

KNTRL=4

KNTRL=3

KNTRL=I

(A)   (B)   (C)   (D)

222

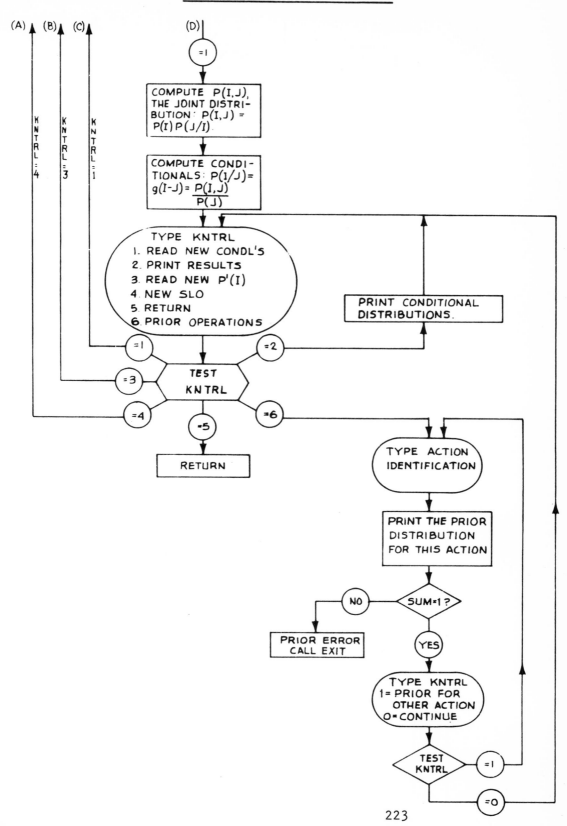

SUBROUTINE STOP

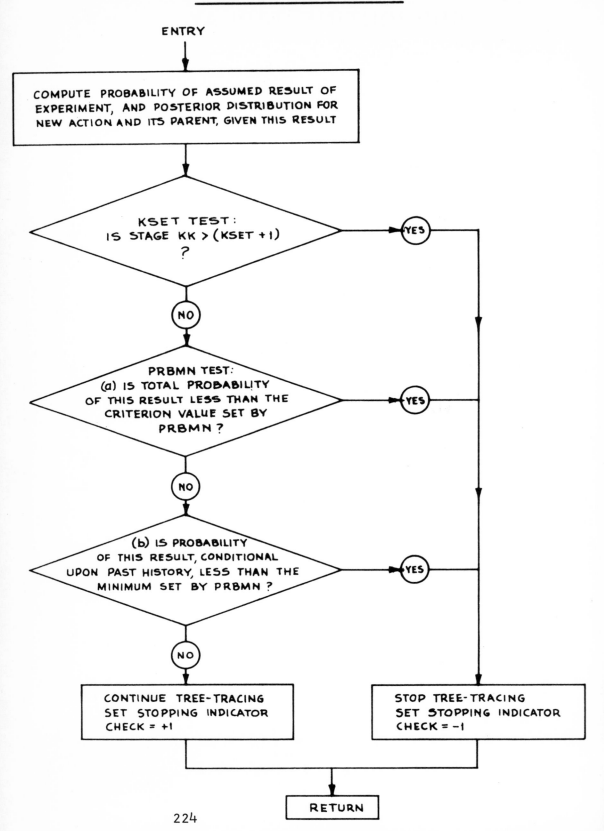

ENTRY

COMPUTE PROBABILITY OF ASSUMED RESULT OF EXPERIMENT, AND POSTERIOR DISTRIBUTION FOR NEW ACTION AND ITS PARENT, GIVEN THIS RESULT

KSET TEST:
IS STAGE KK > (KSET + 1) ?

YES

NO

PRBMN TEST:
(a) IS TOTAL PROBABILITY OF THIS RESULT LESS THAN THE CRITERION VALUE SET BY PRBMN ?

YES

NO

(b) IS PROBABILITY OF THIS RESULT, CONDITIONAL UPON PAST HISTORY, LESS THAN THE MINIMUM SET BY PRBMN ?

YES

NO

CONTINUE TREE-TRACING
SET STOPPING INDICATOR
CHECK = +1

STOP TREE-TRACING
SET STOPPING INDICATOR
CHECK = -1

RETURN

SUBROUTINE TAPLAY

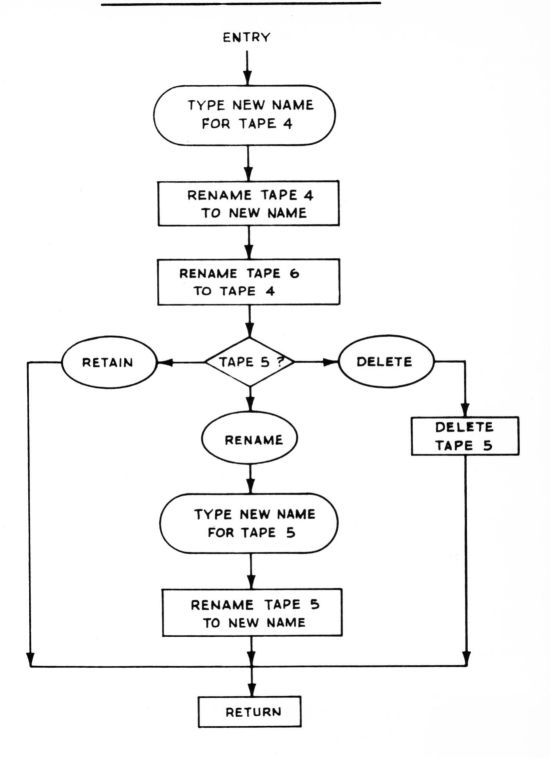

ENTRY

TYPE NEW NAME
FOR TAPE 4

RENAME TAPE 4
TO NEW NAME

RENAME TAPE 6
TO TAPE 4

RETAIN ← TAPE 5 ? → DELETE

RENAME

DELETE
TAPE 5

TYPE NEW NAME
FOR TAPE 5

RENAME TAPE 5
TO NEW NAME

RETURN

SUBROUTINE UPDATE

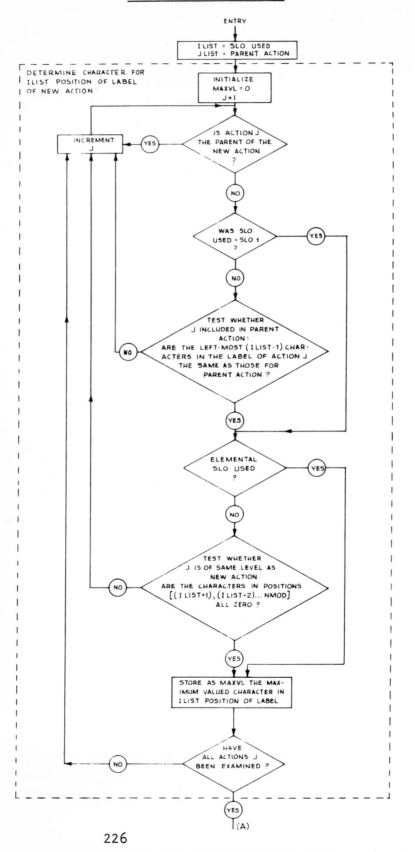

SUBROUTINE UPDATE (CONT'D)

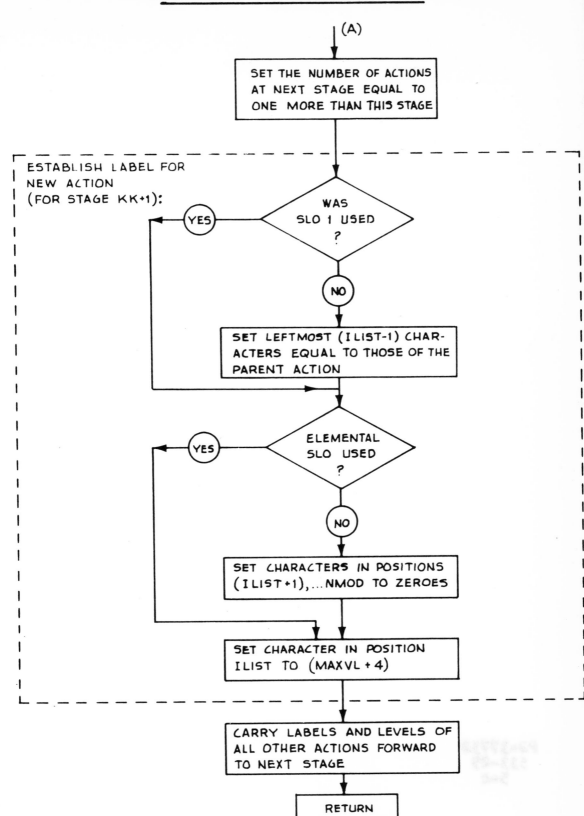

(A)

SET THE NUMBER OF ACTIONS
AT NEXT STAGE EQUAL TO
ONE MORE THAN THIS STAGE

ESTABLISH LABEL FOR
NEW ACTION
(FOR STAGE KK+1):

WAS
SLO 1 USED
?

YES

NO

SET LEFTMOST (ILIST-1) CHAR-
ACTERS EQUAL TO THOSE OF THE
PARENT ACTION

ELEMENTAL
SLO USED
?

YES

NO

SET CHARACTERS IN POSITIONS
(ILIST+1),...NMOD TO ZEROES

SET CHARACTER IN POSITION
ILIST TO (MAXVL + 4)

CARRY LABELS AND LEVELS OF
ALL OTHER ACTIONS FORWARD
TO NEXT STAGE

RETURN

227